THE ECONOMIC
DEFINITION OF ORE

Cut-Off Grades in Theory and Practice

by
Kenneth F. Lane

MINING JOURNAL BOOKS LIMITED
LONDON

Published 1988 by:
Mining Journal Books Ltd., 60 Worship Street,
London, EC2A 2HD, England.
© Mining Journal Books 1988.
ISBN 0 900117 45 1

Text set in 11/13 pt Times Medium Roman by photo-composition and printed offset
litho by Chandlers Printers Ltd., Bexhill-on-Sea, East Sussex, England.

Contents

Background; purpose of book; mining as a staged process; the extraction stage; definition of ore as the extracted material; cut-off grade criterion; economic basis for determination; form of presentation; semantic considerations; significance of finite resource; optimum cut-off grade policies; computer application.

Necessity to analyse the economics of a mining operation; the concept of present value; optimum cut-off grades maximise present values; alternative criteria; importance of capacities; effect of price variations; drawbacks to most breakeven calculations; economic definition of ore.

Formula for present value; dependence upon time, resource remaining and operating strategy; maximum surface and exploitation tracks; optimum strategy tracks; algebraic derivation of maximisation expression; the opportunity cost term and methods of estimation.

Components of a mining system and throughputs; mineralised material, ore and mineral; definitions and discussion; semantics, notation.

Acknowledgements

Many colleagues in the mining industry, particularly within RTZ, have been associated with the work which is described in this book. I should mention especially Mike Blackwell, the engineer who nursed the infant ideas to maturity on their first major application at Bougainville, and also Allen Sykes, who signposted the straight and narrow economic path.

More recently, I have collaborated with RTZ Consultants on several new developments. Mike Mellish has given constant encouragement and Mike Mason, Jim Parker and Dave Hamilton have been enthusiastic contributors.

Throughout, my wife Kath has shown incredible patience while eavesdropping on protracted discussions of incomprehensible subjects like eliminating P and Q, truncating lives, and minimising residual values. Then, in addition, she has spent patient hours with the manuscript on the word processor. Not without good cause does she sometimes refer to me as Ken Cut-off Lane. Her support is appreciated.

Kenneth F. Lane

Foreword

I believe this book is important for three reasons.

First, the topic is important and, although widely researched and taught in mining schools, no authoritative book on the subject has been written.

Second, it is written in a clear manner, which will help even the non-mathematically inclined student or the professional associated with the development of mines.

Finally, with the strong emphasis given to the economics of the whole mining process, and not just the economics of orebodies, the author drives home a lesson often forgotten by the geologist and even the mine planner.

Ken Lane has done a service to the mining industry in writing this book. His early pioneering work some 20 years ago in the RTZ Group brought a new dimension to the world of mining, and I am glad that he has continued his association with the RTZ Consulting Group, which benefits greatly from his advice.

Sir Alistair Frame

NOTATION SUMMARY

Present Value Analysis

Time	T	Short interval	t
Resource Available	R	Small increment	r
Variables defining		Time unit of resource	τ
Exploitation Strategy	Ω	Exploitation Strategy for t	ω

Present Value	$V = V (T, R, \Omega)$ (also W)	
Maximum P.V.	$V^* = V^* (T, R)$	Primes (′)
Opportunity Cost	$F = \delta V^* - dV^*/dT$	indicate
Cash Flow	C per year	net of tax
	c per unit of resource	values
Increment in P.V.	v per unit of resource	
Cost of Capital	δ (100δ %)	
Terminal Value	Γ	

Economic Model

	Throughput	Variable Cost (/unit throughput)	Capacity (throughput/year)
Mining	Material	m	M
Treating	Ore	h	H
Marketing	Mineral	k	K

Fixed or Time costs	f per year
Price	p per unit of material
Cut-off Grade	g mineral/unit of ore
Optimum Cut-offs	G mineral/unit of ore
Average Grade	$\bar{g}$ mineral/unit of ore
Ore/Material Ratio	x
Yield during treatment	y (100y %)
Quantities	q
Stockpile recovery cost	s per unit of material
Stockpile size	S units of material
Cut-off intercepts	γ_1, γ_2 mineral/unit of ore

Suffixes denote years or have particular significance in the context.
Certain other symbols are also used with strictly local definitions.

CHAPTER ONE

Introduction

When I first joined the mining industry I believed that ores, like buried treasures, possessed immediately recognisable characteristics; they glowed in the dark, or glittered in torchlight, or were black and strangely heavy. This is a preconception which is shared by most laymen and I was effectively a layman at the time since my training had been in mathematics and economics, not in mining.

Even after working at several mines, my conviction was unshaken. When the geologists pointed to rich seams in the hanging walls or chipped what they proclaimed as good ore samples from new headings, I attributed my inability to distinguish the material from any of the surrounding rock to my shameful ignorance of mineralogy. I was impressed; these people were sensitive to subtle differences which no amount of concentration revealed to me.

Then, inevitably as a mathematician, I became concerned with the statistics of sampling. I learned that samples are the nerves of operating mines, borehole samples, chip samples, channel samples, grab samples, dust samples — thousands of samples which are regularly taken, assayed, plotted and interpreted. They are the means of mine control and, in the grade control department, they are the means for determining the limits of the ore. At last I understood. Although some ores may be distinguishable by certain physical properties, ores in general are defined operationally by a cut-off grade; material with a mineral content above the cut-off is scheduled for treatment, other material is left or dumped as waste.

Having made this discovery, I asked what seemed to me to be the obvious next question:

Why work to this particular value of cut-off grade rather than some other value?

Typical answers were:
We have always worked to 0·3%.
Head office decided 5% combined metals some years ago.
That is a technical matter; we leave it to the people on-site.
I think several cut-offs were examined in the feasibility study and 1% seemed best.
I guess our costs are running at $10 a tonne and uranium is worth $10 a pound, so 1 lb/tonne must be about right.

The inadequacy of these answers stimulated my original interest in the definition of ore. The fact seemed to be that the subject was not clearly within the scope of any one of the industry's professions — mining, mineral processing, geology or economics — and, as a consequence, had not received the attention which it deserved. I could find no authoritative references, only passing mentions in text books and a few papers. It seemed ironic, in an industry devoted to mining ore, that its definition of ore should be so taken for granted. This was over 20 years ago. Since then I have worked with colleagues, particularly in the RTZ group, on mine design and the economics of cut-off grades for many mines, including several large-scale international operations. In the course of this experience, a theoretical basis for the definition of ore has been established and the theory has been developed to apply to most methods of mining. The applications, particularly to the design of the big mines, have achieved substantial improvements in the overall economics.

The subject is now recognised as important and many people are contributing to its further development. It is on the syllabus of several mining schools and many papers have been written. Yet there is still no single source where the ideas are explained, the formulae quoted, and examples given. Making good this omission is the purpose of this book.

*　　　　　*　　　　　*

Minerals permeate the earth's crust in varying concentrations around the world. A shovel full of soil from most gardens will probably contain measurable amounts of aluminium, silica, potassium, iron, etc. These may be of interest to the gardener but not normally to the miner for the very obvious reason that the concentrations of the mineral are too low.

In fact, concentration is the critical property. The mining industry can be regarded as an industry whose whole concern is with concentration — the progressive concentration of minerals to a form where they become marketable.

Typically the process proceeds in stages. The first stage is exploration, which is the search for mineralised regions in the earth's crust where some degree of natural concentration has already occurred. The second stage is extraction, in which certain parts of a mineralised region are recovered for further treatment. Succeeding stages are treatment stages such as crushing, grinding, flotation, leaching, smelting and refining.

The subdivision of the whole process into stages, and the locations of the exact boundaries between them, is dependent upon the economics of the technologies involved. For example, finer grinding will usually result in better yields of mineral from the ground material but at the expense of higher power consumption. Similarly, better yields will also usually result from longer residence times in leach circuits but at the expense of higher acid consumption. Thus the stages interact and the optimum combination can only be decided with reference to the whole operation.

This book is concerned exclusively with the second stage, extraction. It is often referred to simply as mining, although references to the mining industry are taken to embrace all the stages. The boundary, which is the main focus of attention, is the one which distinguishes the material within a mineralised body that is to be extracted and treated from the remainder. This boundary is normally specified by a cut-off grade.

To avoid ambiguities, the word ore is used solely to describe the material which is extracted for treatment. In other words, by definition, mines extract ore. Hence, establishing an economic basis for determining cut-off grades is, in effect, providing an economic definition of ore.

The form of the presentation is first to enunciate the economic principles which are relevant to the analysis and then to trace the consequences of applying these principles in various circumstances. Although this leads to mathematical complexities in some areas, it transpires that clear and consistent thinking is required more often than agility with algebra. During the course of the work a coherent theory of cut-off grades is developed and the derivations of the main formulae are described in some detail. The intent, however, is to explain the ideas rather than to achieve mathematical rigour. The theory is illustrated with practical case studies which are based upon adaptations of actual applications. Sufficient material is included for the case studies to serve as useful references.

At the outset, problems of semantics are encountered. Many important words are commonly used casually in the industry with different meanings in different contexts. This leads to misunderstandings and has certainly inhibited the development of clear concepts. The word "ore" has already been mentioned and is a prime example. Mineralised bodies are called orebodies before they are mined and even before any serious plans to mine them have been mooted. Then reserves of possible, probable, proven, drilled, inferred and developed ore are often quoted when, strictly speaking, they are estimates of tonnages of mineralised material which could be ore under certain circumstances in the future. In this text, care is taken to avoid such inconsistencies of definition. This sometimes leads to the unfamiliar usage of certain terms, but the intention is not to be pedantic. Only when a distinction is important are abnormal words and usages adopted.

Further problems arise from the finite nature of mineralised bodies. Mining operations based upon them must be of limited duration, a feature which introduces complications into the economic analysis. Unfortunately, it can also introduce an emotional charge into personal attitudes on the subject. These, aggravated by the semantic difficulties, too often result in unedifying arguments rather than useful discussions. Here, problems of this kind are avoided by the strict adherence to the logical consequences of assumptions and objectives. The aim is the development of a definition of ore that is optimum according to accepted current economic ideas, uncompromised by other considerations.

Optimum economic cut-off grade policies have been calculated for a variety of projects over the past 20 years. Broadly, the conclusion in the case of mines which are well established is that these optimum policies seldom differ much from current practices. The reason for this is that the mines have usually been designed, and subsequently perhaps modified, to handle the quantities of ore and mineral and the associated grades to which these practices give rise. The capacities of the equipment and the installations do not often permit much flexibility and therefore cut-off grades can only be varied within narrow limits. In contrast, when expansion schemes are being designed, and even more so when totally new mines are being developed, the theory can indicate cut-off grades quite different from conventional policies with very substantial corresponding improvements in the overall returns.

Although a surprising number of cut-off grade calculations can be done by hand, they can become very intricate. This observation applies particularly to the determination of cut-off policies for long-range planning. In this book these calculations are performed with a computer program which has been developed for the purpose over the years. It is called OGRE (Optimum Grades for Resource Exploitation) and is described in the Appendix (p. 98). The rights to this program are owned by RTZ Consultants.

CHAPTER TWO

Economic Principles

Inevitably, the question that is asked about any body of mineralisation is — Does it contain ore? Or, more strictly — Does it contain any potential ore?

An inconvenient consequence of adopting an economic definition of ore is that there is no longer any inherent property of the mineralised material which permits an answer to this question in isolation. Although exploration personnel often calculate a 'dollar value per ton of rock' in order to assess targets, in fact, minerals in the ground have no explicit value. Not until they have been extracted, treated and delivered to a customer is any value realised. Therefore, the economics of ore definition cannot be assessed separately from the economics of the total mining process. Indeed, it is the economics of the mining process which determine the economic definition of ore.

This point is fundamental. Mineralised bodies are often referred to as valuable resources. In a sense they may be but regarding them as such can be misleading. They are certainly not a valuable resource that might be compared with cash in a bank or even a crop on the ground. The only immediate value they could possess is the price a mining company might bid for the right to mine them. More realistically, a mineralised body should be regarded as a possible opportunity for development, the development being, of course, a mining operation. Any value that might be ascribed to the mineralisation is then realised as an integral part of the proceeds of the operation.

It follows from these considerations that, in order to establish an economic basis for ore definition, the analysis must first be directed to an operating mine. An understanding of the economic factors which influence ore boundaries must be derived from an understanding of the economic factors which influence the whole mining process.

The factors concerned are many and include markets, prices and costs, but they can be integrated using the economic concept of value. A mining operation earns revenue and incurs costs; it is therefore an economic entity and an estimated value can be ascribed to it.

This value is clearly dependent upon the definition of ore, some bases of definition giving rise to higher values than others. The basis which generates the highest value is optimum and this basis establishes the economic definition of the ore. In other words, material from the mineralised body should be scheduled for mining as ore if, and only if, the decision to treat it adds to the overall economic value of the operation. This is the crucial criterion.

Economic value estimates are derived from projected cash flows. As a result of earning revenues and incurring costs year by year, an operation generates annual net cash flows. These can be amalgamated into a value, strictly a 'present' value, by discounting future flows back at an appropriate cost of capital and totalling them.

The theory of present values — or their inverses, internal rates of return — and methods for determining the cost of capital are beyond the scope of the present book. The theory has been widely discussed and analysed in many books and papers and it has been accepted in the mining industry, certainly by its financial analysts. It is almost universally used for valuing properties and evaluating new projects. However, its use as a means to determine an optimum operating policy is less common.

Of course, this does not make it any the less valid, but the unfamiliarity has contributed to scepticism about the present value criterion in this context, particularly when the results differ significantly from conventional ideas. The differences too, are usually that present value maximisation indicates higher grades and higher rates of mining which seem inconsistent with trusted conservative mining policies.

The expression of reservations about the present value criterion, though, is far from proposing an alternative. In fact, alternatives are rarely formulated unambiguously, but the two most general contentions are that:

1) mineralised material should be treated as ore if it will provide a contribution to profit;

2) mining should be conducted in such a way as to maximise the extraction of valuable mineral.

The cut-off policies which result from the application of these criteria can be the same, depending upon the definition of the terms employed, but they are discussed separately.

The first criterion in some form is popular among technical staff. The question of what constitutes a contribution to profit is the subject of much debate, however. It is often argued that any material for which the value of the recovered mineral will exceed the marginal cost of treating it should be ore. Sometimes a contribution towards overheads is added to the costs and sometimes, beyond this, a minimum profit requirement is also added. The basis of the argument is that if such material is not classified as ore, then an opportunity to earn profit has been wasted.

The flaw in the argument is that it totally overlooks capacities. It is equivalent to arguing that a retailer should add to his stock any goods which promise to yield a marginal profit. Retailers do not do this. They are all aware that space is limited and within this limitation they try to stock the more profitable items. Similar considerations apply to a mine. It has a capacity which is limited by some part of the installation — the shaft, the mill, the truck fleet, the rate of development, etc. — and within this limitation it should choose to process the more profitable material. This policy is consistent with the interpretation of the criterion which includes a minimum profit margin, but the supporters of the criterion usually give no basis for determining the margin, other than company policy. The present value criterion, by contrast, gives a precise basis derived as a trade-off between present and future earnings via the present value function.

The second criterion that the extraction of valuable mineral should be maximised is frequently proposed by mineral rights owners, local governments and conservationists. Of course, it immediately begs a question, what is valuable mineral? An extreme argument is that all the mineral or all the geological reserves (whatever they are) should be extracted in the interests of conserving resources. This is an unrealistic stance which usually stems from a misunderstanding of the way in which minerals are distributed in the ground. A less extreme view is that the mine should be developed in such a way that poorer material is extracted along with richer material in an acceptable blend yielding a satisfactory profit. Of course, every mine blends poorer and richer material of necessity and the point of a cut-off grade is to determine just how poor poorer material can be. The protagonists of the maximum extraction criteria, however, usually imply a degree of subsidy for poor material which would not be economic on its own. What this means is unclear, but the idea of cross-subsidies of ore grades is economically unsound except in special circumstances. A more reasonable view defines valuable material in the same way as in the first criterion. In this case the two give the same result and suffer from the same objection about the effects of capacity.

Both of the criteria have another major shortcoming; they do not deal satisfactorily with price variations. Nor do they deal satisfactorily with variations in other economic parameters, but price is the predominant influence.

The point is that, as with all break-even calculations which compare inherent value with cost in some form, higher prices lead to lower cut-off grades. Now, lower cut-off grades yield lower average grades and if the quantity of ore treated remains the same, as it most often does, the output of mineral declines. This is quite the reverse of what should happen in the market. Higher prices imply a deficiency of supply in relation to demand and should prompt an increase in supply, not a decrease. Further, the mine itself is in the position of selling less at the higher price than the lower, a policy which cannot make sense.

Present value is the only criterion which does incorporate a means for dealing with varying economic conditions. Parameters defining the conditions are included in the present value estimates and affect the optimum cut-off calculations in a way which avoids nonsensical

9

reactions to price changes. This feature is illustrated in Case Study 2 (p. 112).

Many of the criticisms of the present value criterion are actually expressions of special interests. For example, it is rarely advantageous for the staff of an operating mine to support a policy which shortens its life; they would only be threatening their own livelihoods. Similarly, local governments usually wish to see industrial activities prolonged because this entails continuing employment, continuing taxes and, perhaps, continuing royalties.

There is an apparent conflict here between the interests of the contributing parties but, from a strictly economic point of view, it is not an inevitable conflict. If a mine is planned in such a way as to maximise its net present value (excess of present value over capital costs) then, in theory, there is more wealth to share between the participants. Everyone could be better off. Whether, in the event, they are or not depends upon the nature of the agreements between them, but this is a huge subject in its own right.

To repeat, this book is concerned wholly with the economic definition of ore as that definition which maximises the net present value of a mining operation. There may well be reasons, in special cases, for adopting other bases of definition, necessarily sub-optimum, but such cases are not covered in this book except for occasional incidental references.

CHAPTER THREE

Finite Resources and Present Values

As has been stressed already, every mine is established on a body of mineralisation which is ultimately of limited extent. Some are very localised and are mined out in a matter of months; others are vast with seemingly endless sources of ore. Nonetheless, they are actually finite and, sooner or later, will be depleted.

This characteristic makes the analysis of operating strategies for mines very different from the analysis for most other industrial or commercial undertakings. The fundamental concept of optimisation by maximising present values is just as relevant. However, other undertakings are not usually based upon an exhaustable resource and, hence, current operating strategies do not react on the future in the same way. For a mine, higher mining rates will shorten the life and vice versa. The effects of this must somehow be built into the analysis. It is, of course, the present value function itself which provides the means for making cash effects, which occur at different times, commensurate. An essential preliminary to an analysis of cut-off strategy is, therefore, an examination of present value maximisation for an operation based upon a finite resource. This necessarily involves some mathematics but detailed explanations are also given in the following paragraphs.

Denote the present value of an operation based upon a finite resource by V. The operation could be a mine but the analysis is general and could apply to any type of finite resource operation like, for example, the liquidation of a stockpile.

V is calculated as the total of the future cash flows discounted back to the present. If these cash flows, year by year, are $C_1, C_2, \ldots$ and the cost of capital is δ ($100 \times \delta$ as a percentage) then

$$V = C_1/(1 + \delta) + C_2/(1 + \delta)^2 + \ldots$$

The cash flows C_1, C_2, . . . are dependent on the prices and costs prevailing at the time and therefore the value of V itself is dependent upon the present time, T, which forms the base of the calculation. In other words, the present value of two exactly similar operations calculated at different times will, in general, differ.

$$\text{i.e. } V = V(T)$$

Further, the present value must also depend upon the amount of resource, R, still available. In general, it must decline as the resource is consumed and fall to zero when the resource is exhausted.

$$\text{i.e. } V = V(T,R) \text{ and } V(T,0) = 0$$

This, however, is not the end of the story. V must depend upon many more variables which describe the way in which the operation is to be conducted. Rather than writing a long list, a convenient mathematical convention is to represent these variables by one symbol. Call it Ω. Ω defines the operating strategies to be employed in the future and

$$V = V(T,R,\Omega)$$

In the case of cut-off strategies for a mine, Ω would consist of the variable cut-off (g, say) which can take on different values, g_1, g_2, g_3, . . . for the remaining years of the mine's life. Such a sequence of values can be called a policy and therefore g_1, g_2, g_3, . . . define a cut-off policy. Thus, in this case, if cut-off grades are the only parameters being investigated,

$$\Omega = g_1, g_2, \ldots$$
$$V = V(T,R,g_1,g_2, \ldots)$$

Now, reverting to the general case, of all the sets of operating strategies, Ω, which could be adopted, there must be one set, at least, which is optimum in the sense that this set gives rise to the maximum value for $V(T,R,\Omega)$. Or, to put it another way, any set of values for Ω

will give rise to some value for $V(T,R,\Omega)$, and if Ω is varied over every conceivable set of values, $V(T,R,\Omega)$ will vary correspondingly, and one, at least, of the values it assumes must be maximum.

Call this maximum $V^*(T,R)$. A significant observation is that it is no longer a function of Ω. $V(T,R,\Omega)$ itself was, but $V^*(T,R)$ is not. This is like observing that heights on a map are a function of position but the height of the highest point is not. It has a position, of course, but it is dependent only upon the particular area covered by the map, nothing else.

$$\text{Max}_\Omega\{V(T,R,\Omega)\} = V^*(T,R)$$

Before developing the algebra further, consider the function $V^*(T,R)$ more closely. It is a function of two variables and therefore forms a surface. For $R = 0$, when the resource is exhausted, $V^* = 0$ so the surface slopes to zero along the $R = 0$ axis. Also, the function must decrease, in general, as R decreases (only if the optimum strategy involves a cash outflow will it increase).

A possible surface is shown in figure 3.1 and an understanding of this figure is important. The surface it represents consistently slopes down towards the lower axis on which the resource available is zero. This axis is itself the zero 'present value' contour. Moving across the figure, the contours form a ridge along the vertical axis at time zero, decline into a shallow valley with a floor between three and four years and then rise gently, apparently flattening to a plateau, beyond ten years.

For example, if the operation has 8 million tonnes of resource available now $(T = 0)$, its present value interpolating by eye is $4·25 million. In 3½ years time, if the operation has been inactive in the interim so that the resource available remains 8 million tonnes, the present value will have decreased to about $3·4 million. Thereafter, it gradually increases to over $5 million after 10 years.

A pattern of this kind arises from projections of prices and costs which deteriorate initially and then persistently improve. Projections of constant prices and costs give rise to horizontal parallel values which imply that present values are not affected unless some resource is consumed.

13

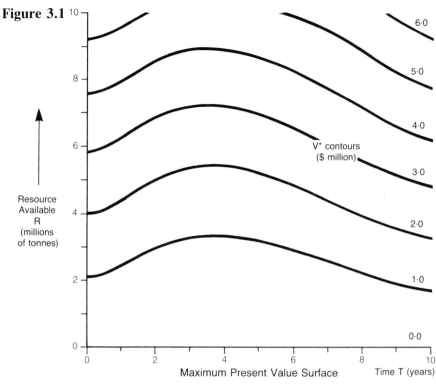

Figure 3.1

Resource Available R (millions of tonnes)

V* contours ($ million)

6·0

5·0

4·0

3·0

2·0

1·0

0·0

Maximum Present Value Surface

Time T (years)

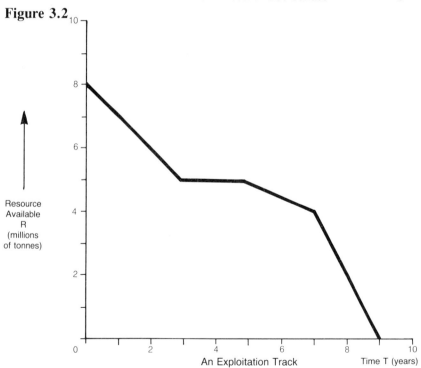

Figure 3.2

Resource Available R (millions of tonnes)

An Exploitation Track

Time T (years)

Of the two independent variables T and R, the former is not controllable. It is simply the date on which the present value is based, i.e. it defines the present to which cash flows are discounted. The latter, R, or more exactly the rate at which R is decremented, is the variable which is directly affected by operations.

Of course, as R is decremented (that is, as resource is consumed), time necessarily progresses and the changing resource level with time can be graphed. It forms a line or track as is illustrated in figure 3.2. This track defines the rate at which the resource is consumed at every moment throughout the life of the operation and hence it is a complete specification of an exploitation strategy. It can be called an exploitation track.

The track illustrated in figure 3.2 implies that the operation starts with resources of 8 million tonnes, produces at a rate of 1 million tonnes per year for the first three years, is shut for two years, reopens at 0·5 million tonnes per year for the next two years and finally produces at a rate of 2 million tonnes a year until exhausted at the end of nine years.

Every exploitation track has an associated sequence of present values. Given the projected prices, costs and other economic parameters, the cash flows for each year can be calculated and from them the present values at every point along the track can be compiled.

These present values can be compared with those at the corresponding points on the maximum present value surface. Obviously, none can exceed the corresponding maximum and in general they will all be less. When equality occurs, the remainder of the track from the point of equality onwards defines an optimum strategy track. Moreover, the present values at every subsequent point along such a track must also equal the corresponding maxima; if not, an alternative track yielding a higher present value could be constructed in contradiction to the definition of the maximum.

This principle is fundamental. An optimum strategy track must be optimum for every point along its length and all the associated present values must be maxima. In other words, optimum strategy tracks must be embedded in the maximum present value surface. In

Figure 3.3

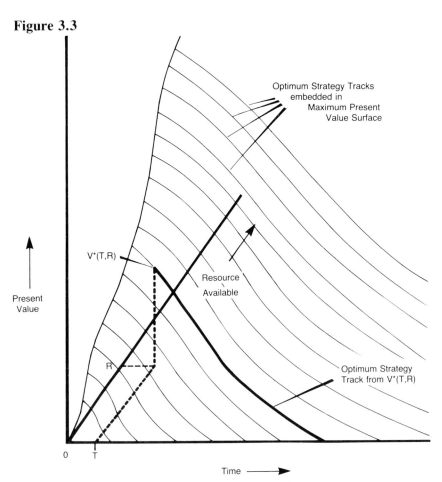

Three Dimensional Representation of Optimum
Strategy Tracks Embedded in
Maximum Present Value Surface

general they form a series of parallel lines within the surface as illustrated in figure 3.3. (Mathematically, the application of this principle of optimality is known as dynamic programming).

In order to find an optimum operating strategy and the corresponding maximum present value in a particular case, the totality of the maximum present value surface is irrelevant. Only the surface in the immediate vicinity of the track matters. If some way of deciding the direction of the track at any stage can be found then, given some starting point, the track can be followed and its associated present values compiled. This is the purpose of the following analysis.

Reverting to the algebra and starting with resource R at time T, consider a small decrement of r in R. Let the operating strategy for effecting this decrement be defined by ω. Let the time taken be t and let the corresponding cash flow per unit of resource be c. t is a function of ω and r, and c is a function of ω and t

$$\text{i.e. } t = t(\omega,r) \quad \text{and } c = c(\omega,t)$$

After taking the decrement, r, the resource remaining will be $R-r$ and the time $T+t$. This will have a present value

$$V = V(T+t,R-r,\Omega')$$

where Ω' is the operating strategy adopted from this point onwards. The present value at T,R may be denoted by

$$V = V(T,R,\omega+\Omega')$$

because the corresponding operating strategy is ω for the decrement r followed by Ω'.

By definition of present values

$$V(T,R,\omega+\Omega') = rc(\omega,t) + V(T+t,R-r,\Omega')/(1+\delta)^t$$

where δ is the cost of capital (100δ as a percentage).

If ω is to be an optimum strategy for the decrement r and part of an optimum strategy Ω, then Ω' must constitute an optimum strategy and

$$V(T+t,R-r,\Omega') = V^*(T+t,R-r)$$

17

Now, maximising both sides of the equation with respect to ω

$$V^*(T,R) = \text{Max} \{rc(\omega,t) + V^*(T+t,R-r)/(1+\delta)^t\}$$

but expanding by the binomial theorem and assuming r and t small,

$$V^*(T+t,R-r)/(1+\delta)^t = \{V^*(T,R) + tdV^*/dT - rdV^*/dR\}(1-\delta t)$$
$$= (1-\delta t)V^*(T,R) + tdV^*/dT - rdV^*/dR$$

to the first order of approximation and assuming the differentials are at the point T,R.

Hence, dropping the T,R dependence to simplify the notation

$$V^* = \text{Max} \{rc(\omega,t) + V^* - \delta tV^* + tdV^*/dT - rdV^*/dR\}$$

However, both V^* and rdV^*/dR are independent of ω and may be removed from the maximisation expression. V^* cancels and

$$rdV^*/dR = \text{Max} \{rc(\omega,t) + t(dV^*/dT - \delta V^*)\}$$

Here dV^*/dT, like V^*, is also independent of ω.

Putting $F = \delta V^* - dV^*/dT$ the equation may be rewritten

$$rdV^*/dR = \text{Max} \{rc-Ft\} \text{ or } dV^*/dR = \text{Max} \{c-Ft/r\}$$

where F is constant and the maximisation is with respect to ω.

This equation is a quite remarkable result. It implies that dV^*/dR must be a maximum at all points along an optimum strategy track. This means that the strategies must be chosen so that every decrement r in R has the greatest possible effect on V^*. This is intuitively obvious because summing all the changes in V^*, corresponding to a sequence of decrements in R, all the way to zero will then give the greatest total. Or, in reverse, if an optimum strategy track is followed backwards from R = 0 in steps of r, then, if each step is taken in the direction of steepest ascent up surface V^*, the final point reached must be the highest possible.

The remarkable features, however, are on the right-hand side of the equation.

Firstly the maximisation is no more difficult than the maximisation of c itself. The only difference introduced by considering the present value of a sequence of cash flows instead of each cash flow individually is the addition of the term Ft. As F is independent of ω, this is equivalent to the addition of a time cost term and one term of this nature is almost certainly already in c.

Secondly, in order to determine the optimum exploitation strategy at any point, the only information that is required from the remainder of the optimisation process in the future is the value of F. A simultaneous maximisation for all the variables in Ω is not necessary. This is a vast simplification although, of course, F is dependent upon the future strategy, so some method of determining its value has still to be developed.

In economic parlance, the term F is an opportunity cost. The operation can be regarded as having a capital value of V. Indeed, this is one interpretation of present value. It is, in a sense, capital which incurs two penalties as a result of being tied up in the operation. One is the interest that could have been earned were it deployed elsewhere; this is δV, δ being the corporation's cost of capital. The other is the decline in value as a consequence of deteriorating economic conditions; this is $-dV^*/dT$ (it can, of course, be a bonus rather than a penalty if dV^*/dT is positive).

There are two main alternative methods for determining a value for F in practical applications.

The first method is simply to estimate it. This method is satisfactory when the cash flows are not oversensitive to changes in operating strategy and only a current optimum is required. In these circumstances an approximation for F gives an adequate basis for establishing the optimum because errors in the estimate have little significant effect on the result. Moreover F, however it is determined, is only an economic projection which is subject to a measure of uncertainty. This subject is discussed in Chapter 8.

The second method is to employ a mathematical iteration technique. A starting value for F is assumed and a complete optimum exploitation strategy calculated, step by step, until all the resource is exhausted. The residual present value at this stage should be zero. If it is not, the starting value for F is adjusted and the process repeated. A technique of this kind is well suited to computer applications and has the advantage of deriving a complete exploitation strategy which, in certain cases, can be important. Chapter 10 describes the technique in the context of determining an optimum cut-off grade policy.

Summarising, the optimum exploitation strategy for maximising the present value of an operation based upon a finite resource can be determined at any stage by maximising the expression

$$c - \tau(\delta V^* - dV^*/dT) = c - F\tau \ldots (I)$$

where c is the cash flow arising from a unit decrement of resource, τ is the time taken to process the unit and V^* is the maximum present value at that stage. This formula is necessary for the calculation of optimum cut-off grades in conjunction with a suitable economic model.

CHAPTER FOUR

Economic Models

The purpose of an economic model of an operation is to provide a means for calculating the effects of changes in certain variables. For present purposes, it is necessary to be able to calculate the effects of changes in cut-off grades, throughputs, prices and costs on the cash flows from a mining operation. Mines differ in many ways and sometimes have unique features so that mine models often have to be specially tailored to fit the circumstances. However, the structure of the mining process is similar in most applications and it is useful to construct a basic model to which variations can be made as necessary.

There are three main components to a mining operation related to the throughput with which the component is concerned. The three throughputs are:
1) Mineralised material
2) Ore
3) Mineral
The definition of components in this way is fundamental but the interpretation of the definition differs for various types of mine.

1) Mineralised Material
This component can be called the mining component. It is concerned with creating access to the interior of the mineralised body. Costs are incurred per tonne of mineralised material made accessible and capacity is the maximum rate at which the mineralised body can be opened up.

In an underground mine this component would normally be called development. It consists of driving headings, raises etc. and forming stopes in preparation for the extraction of ore. In an open pit it is the drilling, blasting and hauling of material since access is gained by total excavation.

2) Ore
This can be called the treatment component. It is concerned with the further processing of that part of the mineralised body which is determined to be ore. The costs are incurred per tonne of ore and the capacity is the maximum throughput of ore that the installation can handle.

Underground, most of the extraction process, which is normally referred to as mining, comes into this category because, usually, only the ore is extracted. The remainder of the mineralised body is left in place. Hoisting and concentrating also belong to this category. In an open pit the definition is clearer. It is the process through which the ore passes after it has been hauled from the pit.

The capacity of a mine is normally quoted as the capacity of the ore treatment component of the operation. For example, a 3,000 tonnes per day mine is understood to be one which can process up to 3,000 tonnes per day of ore. The reason for this convention is that ore handling and concentrating are usually the most capital intensive sections of the mining installations and, more often than any others, they are the final limiting factors on output.

3) Mineral
This can be called the marketing component although it might well include smelting and refining as well as selling. The costs are incurred per unit of mineral and the associated capacity is a limit on the output of mineral. Refineries and smelters often impose such a limit. Markets, too, sometimes have an upper bound. This component is essentially the same for all types of mine. Figure 4.1 summarises these definitions graphically.

It is important to appreciate that these definitions of the main components in mining do entail significant departures from normal usage in the interpretation of certain words. The reason for this is the

Figure 4.1

	UNDERGROUND	SURFACE
MINING	Developing Raising Cross-cutting	Drilling and blasting Loading Hauling
	Stoping Tramming Hoisting	
TREATING	Crushing Grinding Separating	
MARKETING	Smelting Refining Selling	

need to develop a model consistent with both underground and surface applications and to accommodate the three component structure.

For example, in an underground operation, stoping and tramming would normally be classified as mining because they are underground activities which are the responsibility of the mining department. Hoisting is more doubtful but it, too, is normally classified as mining. In this analysis, however, all three activities are classified as treatment activities because they are concerned with ore. The point is that material within the mineralised body only incurs stoping, tramming and hoisting costs if it is classified as ore; otherwise it is usually left in place and incurs no further cost.

Development is normally a clearly recognised activity underground. It is the process of creating access to the mineralised body and generally the material cannot be adequately sampled to determine its grade and decide whether or not it is to be ore until sufficient access has been gained. Therefore, development costs are incurred per unit of mineralised material opened up. Raising, cross-cutting and often some stope preparation costs are also essentially access costs. Here, they are all classified as mining costs for consistency with surface applications.

In open pit parlance, stripping is the nearest equivalent to a pure development cost because it is incurred only to gain access to the mineralised body. However, on closer examination it is clear that all mining activities have an access function; even when the material removed is ore, its removal is still essential to reach the material beneath it. Treatment costs are only incurred when material classified as ore starts to attract costs beyond those incurred by waste. Hence, practically all the mining costs are access costs per unit of material within the pit, and this is why the term has been adopted in this text.

Mineralised body is another term where the definition requires some care. It is the total envelope within which mining is planned. In an open pit context it is everything within the ultimate open pit. Underground it is the whole region within the mining leases to which development is planned to extend. A mineralised body contains mineralised material, by definition, but normally some of it will be of zero grade — for example, overburden and dykes — and only a proportion of the remainder will prove to be economic and hence treated as ore.

These definitions have been elaborated at length because they have proved to be a source of some confusion. Most professional miners know what mining costs are by their own definitions and they do not readily adapt to the idea that for cut-off grade determinations such costs should, in certain circumstances, be renamed.

Semantics are really the whole problem. The practicalities are that the development of a suitable cost model for any mine requires a special study to determine the fixed and variable elements that are relevant for the ranges of variation under study. For cut-off analyses, the variable elements, whatever they are called, must be related to the three throughputs, mineralised material, ore, and mineral.

In general there are substantial fixed elements in what are reported as mining, treatment, or marketing costs and these must be estimated, separated and aggregated with the more normally accepted fixed costs such as administration and overheads. Strictly, of course, the word "fixed" in this context is another loose term; such costs vary with time and are more properly called time costs.

A convenient notation is:

Component	Throughput	Basic Quantity	Variable cost (/unit thro'put)	Capacity (thro'put/yr)
Mining	Mineralised Material	1	m	M
Treating	Ore	x	h	H
Marketing	Mineral	x$\bar{g}$	k	K

where x is the proportion of mineralised material classified as ore and $\bar{g}$ is the average grade of the ore as a mineral : ore ratio.

Other variables are:
  g cut-off grade applied to mineralised material to define ore (mineral ore ratio).
  y yield of mineral in the treatment process (100 y%)
  f time costs per year (sometimes referred to as fixed costs).
  p price per unit of mineral.
  c cash flow per unit of mineralised material.
  τ time taken to work through one unit of mineralised material.
Any of these parameters can vary from year to year and this can be represented by quoting the years as suffixes. Other suffixes are also used in the text; their significance is dependent upon the context.

Using this notation, the formula for the cash flow arising from one unit of mineralised material is

$$c = (p-k)xy\bar{g}-xh-m-f\tau \ . \ . \ . \ (II)$$

where τ is the time taken to progress through the unit. τ depends upon which of the three components of the mining operation is actually limiting throughput. Thus, three cases have now to be examined and this is the subject of the next chapter.

Although the majority of the analysis in the remainder of the book is concentrated on the model represented by Expression II, other models can be adopted. The special importance of Expression II is that it is the simplest model which reveals the basic revenue and cost structure of a mining operation.

In an application a model which is faithful to the mine under study should always be constructed. The principles of the subsequent analysis will remain the same but some of the results may differ.

Examples of some other models are given in Chapter 17.

CHAPTER FIVE

Limiting Economic Cut-Off Grades

Having derived an expression to be maximised in order to obtain an optimum operating strategy for an undertaking based upon a finite resource (I), and having derived a formula relating cash flows to cut-off grades for a mine (II), it is now possible to combine the two and to quote an expression for determining optimum cut-off grades. It is:

$$\text{Max}_g\{(p-k)xy\bar{g}-xh-m-f\tau-\tau(\delta V^*-dV^*/dT)\}$$
$$\text{or } \text{Max}_g\{(p-k)xy\bar{g}-xh-m-(f+F)\tau\}$$

For future reference call the expression in brackets v.

$$\text{i.e. } v = (p-k)xy\bar{g}-xh-m-(f+F)\tau \ldots \text{(III)}$$

It corresponds to dV^*/dR, the rate at which the present value is changing with respect to changes in R, the resource available.

In this expression x, the ore to mineralised material ratio, and $\bar{g}$, the average grade, are directly dependent upon the cut-off, g. The time τ, is also dependent upon g, but indirectly, and three cases must be recognised according to the capacity which is limiting output. The three cases give rise to three optimum cut-off grades which are called limiting economic cut-off grades.

The data from Case Study 3 (p.116) are used to illustrate the results. The operation concerned is a medium-sized open pit uranium mine. For ease of reference, the relevant figures are also presented here:

Mining variable cost $1·32/tonne of material (m)
Treating variable cost $3·41/tonne of ore (h)

Mining capacity	12 million tonnes/year (M)
Treating capacity	3·9 million tonnes/year (H)
Marketing capacity	0·9 thousand tonnes/year (K)
Fixed costs	$11·9 million/year (f)
Price net of marketing costs	$60 per kilo (p)
Recovery	0·87 (y)
Estimated opportunity cost	$15·2 million (F)

1) Mine Limiting

With the rate of mining (O/P) or the rate of development (U/G) limiting throughput, the corresponding capacity is M units per year so the time to handle one unit is 1/M. Hence the expression becomes

$$\text{Max}_g\{v_m = (p-k)xy\bar{g}-xh-m-(f+F)/M\}$$

Only the terms $(p-k)xy\bar{g}-xh$ vary with g so g_m, the optimum cut-off with the mine limiting, is given by

$$\text{Max}_g\{x[(p-k)y\bar{g}-h]\}$$

Here $\bar{g}$ and x can be represented by integrals of the grade distribution function and the maximum determined by calculus. However, it is possible to see, because of the form of the expression $x\{(p-k)y\bar{g}-h\}$, that g can be lowered for as long as $(p-k)yg$ is greater than h. Hence the breakeven point is given by

$$(p-k)yg_m = h$$
$$\text{or } g_m = h/(p-k)y$$

This is effectively the same breakeven concept that is employed in other determinations of cut-off grades; mineralised material should be classified as ore for as long as its implicit value, $(p-k)yg$, exceeds the cost of further processing, h.

There are two significant features of the formula for g_m.

First, it means that the implicit value of mineralised material need only cover the variable cost of treatment (after due allowance for marketing cost, k). Time costs are not relevant and neither is the development nor mining cost. This is so because the formula has been derived on the assumption that the decision to continue operating beyond the current time horizon had already been taken. If it had not, different considerations apply. These are illustrated in Case Study 1 (p.108).

Secondly, it does not involve any reference to present values. This means that a mine limited by its mining or development capacity in this way should be operated on a tactical rather than a strategic basis. There is no trade-off of future losses against present gains to modify current policies.

For instance, on a tactical basis, if the mineral price changes, the cut-off grade should be changed and in the manner criticised as illogical earlier; namely, as the price rises the grade should be lowered. There is no illogicality in this case because a lower grade increases the proportion of mineralised material classified as ore and hence the total mineral produced; there is no restriction on the treatment capacity to limit the throughput of the extra ore. Therefore, output rises as the price rises.

Substituting the data presented above

$$g_m = 3 \cdot 41/60 \times 0 \cdot 87$$
$$= 0 \cdot 07 \text{ kilo/tonne}$$

A cut-off of $0 \cdot 07$ kilo/tonne is actually very low. It arises because if the mine is limiting, the treatment plant and market are starved of throughput so everything possible is classified as ore.

2) Treatment Limiting

This is the common case with either the ore handling facilities or the concentrating plant restricting throughput. In this case, one unit of mineralised material gives rise to x units of ore and these take x/H units of time to treat. Therefore $\tau = x/H$ and the expression becomes

$$\text{Max}_g\{v_h = (p-k)xy\bar{g}-xh-m-(f+F)x/H\}$$

Following the same reasoning as before, this is equivalent to

$$\text{Max}_g\{x[(p-k)y\bar{g}-h-(f+F)/H]\}$$

29

and g_h is given by

$$(p-k)yg_h = h + (f+F)/H$$
$$\text{or } g_h = \{h + (f+F)/H\}/(p-k)y$$

This illustrates the point that the present value term

$F = \delta V^* - dV^*/dT$, appears simply as an additional time cost.

This formula is very different from any traditional formula because of the presence of the term F, which can be very significant. Notice that the cut-off grade declines as F declines, which it normally does as the mine ages. This is a particular characteristic of optimum cut-offs determined by the present theory.

Again, substituting the data presented above

$$g_h = \{3.41 + (11.9 + 15.2)/3.9\} / 60 \times 0.87$$
$$= 0.20 \text{ kilo/tonne}$$

This is a much higher cut-off than that obtained when the mine is limiting. Without the opportunity cost, F ($=15.2$), the formula would give

$$g = \{3.41 + 11.90/3.9\} / 60 \times 0.87$$
$$= 0.12 \text{ kilo/tonne}$$

This figure is probably similar to those derived from traditional cut-off grade analyses which take no account of present value maximisation. The difference illustrates the premium attaching to earlier cash flows when only the treatment facilities are limiting throughput.

3) Market Limiting

This can be a genuine market restriction imposed by, say, an exclusive sales contract or it can be the limiting capacity of a refinery or smelter. One unit of mineralised material gives rise to $xy\bar{g}$ units of mineral which take $xy\bar{g}/K$ units of time to process or sell. Thus, the optimising expression becomes

$$\text{Max}_g \{v_k = (p-k)xy\bar{g}-xh-m-(f+F)xy\bar{g}/K\}$$

As before this is equivalent to

$$\text{Max}_g\ \{x[(p-k-(f+F)/K)y\bar{g}-h]\}$$

and g_k is given by

$$\{p-k-(f+F)/K\}yg_k = h$$
$$\text{or } g_k = h/\{p-k-(f+F)/K\}y$$

This and the preceding formulae have in common the property that the fixed costs have been distributed according to the limiting capacity and added to the corresponding variable cost: i.e. for the treatment limiting case, the treatment cost becomes

$$h + (f+F)/H$$

and for the market limiting case, the marketing cost becomes

$$k + (f+F)/K$$

The latter formula is novel in form but it possesses the same typical characteristic that the cut-off grade declines as F declines as the remaining life of the mine is reduced.

Applying this formula to the uranium mine data given earlier on page 27

$$g_k = 3\cdot41\ /\ \{60-(11\cdot9+15\cdot2)/0\cdot9\} \times 0\cdot87$$
$$= 0\cdot11 \text{ kilo/tonne}$$

This lower figure is a consequence of the fact that a market limitation restricts the extent to which the cash flow pattern can be influenced by the cut-off grade policy.

For illustrative purposes, the same value for the opportunity cost has been used in all three cases. This is somewhat artificial because the three assumptions about which component is actually limiting the throughput would, if they were applied to the life of the operation, give rise to three different outcomes with correspondingly different opportunity costs. However, the $15·2 million derived in Case Study 3 (p.116) is a typical figure for a mine of this kind and its use gives results which are realistic and comparable. They reveal the profound effects which capacities have on cut-off grade determinations.

None of these formulae makes any direct reference to the mineral grades actually present in the mineralised body. Neither do other breakeven formulae. A cut-off grade is calculated with reference solely to costs, prices and capacities quite regardless of the way the grades actually vary within the mineralised body being mined.

This characteristic, although well accepted within the industry, is nevertheless one which is intuitively unlikely. Surely the cut-off grade must, in general, depend upon the particular grade distribution of the mineralised body under consideration? The answer, in general, is yes and the way in which this actual mineralised grade distribution impinges on the optimum cut-off grade is the subject of the next chapter. However, in the particular situation where only one component of the mining system limits throughput, the fact is that the actual grade distribution is not directly relevant.

The application of these limiting economic cut-off grade formulae is illustrated in the first three Case Studies. The second and third require estimates of present values. This subject is dealt with in Chapter 8 but, for the purpose of the Case Studies, suitable estimates have been obtained in simple but not unrealistic ways.

One very important reservation about the application of these formulae and, indeed, about the application of any other breakeven formulae is that they apply to actual grades as they occur in the ground. These are not necessarily identical with the grades as measured for the implementation of a cut-off grade decision. It is a common assumption that they are but it is not one which is generally valid. For example, grade control may be exercised on the basis of one mineral although the value of the ore may be a composite of several minerals. Also there may be significant grade measurement errors. Both of these cause discrepancies between the theoretical boundary between ore and waste given by the breakeven formulae and the actual separation achieved in practice by the imposition of the breakeven grade as an operational cut-off grade. In these circumstances, the operational cut-off grade is called a parametric cut-off because it is indirectly related to the real grade. Limiting economic cut-off grades still exist but must be calculated with care. This subject is discussed more fully in Chapter 11.

Another reservation is that the formulae are dependent upon the form of Equation II. A different model giving rise to a different equation will generally have maxima determined by different formulae. They have to be derived specially for each case. If this should prove difficult because of the form of the equation, the maxima can always be found by a search process. This possibility is mentioned in several contexts and also described in Chapter 11. An example of different maximisation formulae is given in Chapter 17.

CHAPTER SIX

Balancing Cut-Off Grades

In the preceding chapter, cases were considered where one component limited the throughput of the mining system. In these cases the optimum cut-off grade was shown to be uniquely determined by economic factors and was called a limiting cut-off grade. In general, though, as in any system with several components, no single component is limiting. In these cases, two, and sometimes all three, components are said to be in balance.

The factors which determine the relative utilisation of capacities in a mining system are the grade distribution of the material being mined and the cut-off grade which is being applied to that mined material.

A low cut-off implies that most of the material being developed and made accessible is treated as ore. The recovery of mineral from the total mineralised body is high because very little is classified as waste but the average grade of the ore is low. Hence, the amount of mineral obtained from a given extent of development is high but the mineral production from a given throughput of ore is low.

A high cut-off implies high selectivity in mining which requires a high rate of development to maintain a given level of ore feed. The recovery of mineral from a given extent of development is comparatively low because the lower grades of mineralisation are classified as waste but the average grade of the ore is high so that mineral production from a given throughput of ore is high.

Intermediate cut-off grades give rise to intermediate positions and, in general, there are values at which the capacities are fully utilised in pairs. These are called balancing cut-off grades.

The existing capacities of the mining system thus limit the range of possible cut-off grades and hence effectively prescribe the choice. To see more clearly how this occurs, the concept of balancing cut-off grades must be examined in a little more detail.

The simplest illustration of the concept is perhaps provided by an open pit operation based upon a disseminated mineralised body. The mineralised material will consist of a range of grades which, in practice, will have been estimated for a mining increment covering at least several weeks ahead by a sampling process, probably blasthole sampling. A grade distribution can be constructed for this sampled material by calculating the proportions that exceed a range of grade limits. The result is a graph called a Cumulative Grade Distribution which has the shape illustrated in figure 6.1. Obviously, 100% of the material exceeds a grade of zero but the proportion declines steadily as the grade limit increases from this value.

An open pit has a maximum capacity for moving material imposed by the size of its truck fleet and the number of shovels and drills. It is M units per year. Similarly, the treatment plant has a maximum handling capacity for handling ore, H units per year. These two components will therefore balance when the quantity of ore arising from a given quantity of mineralised material is in the ratio of H:M; in other words, the ore:material ratio is H/M.

Returning to the Cumulative Grade Distribution graph, because it declines steadily there must be a point along its length at which the proportion of mineralised material above the corresponding grade exactly equals the ratio H/M. The grade at this point is called the mine/treatment plant balancing cut-off grade, g_{mh}, because operating at this cut-off keeps the two components simultaneously at full capacity. This is shown in figure 6.1.

The same sample results permit the calculation, not only of the proportions of mineralised material above a range of grade limits, but also the recoverable mineral contents of these proportions. This graph takes a similar form, as in figure 6.2. Again the graph declines continuously because, within a given quantity of mineralised material, the higher the grade limit the less mineral exceeds it. (The total mineral content should not be confused with the average

Figure 6.1

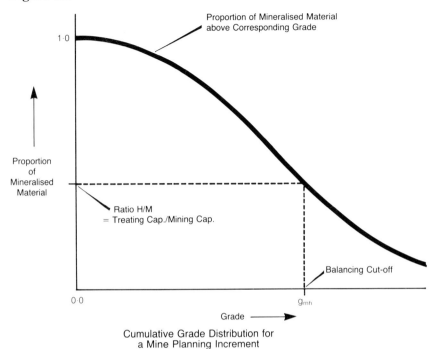

Proportion of Mineralised Material above Corresponding Grade

1·0

Proportion of Mineralised Material

Ratio H/M = Treating Cap./Mining Cap.

Balancing Cut-off

0·0

g_{mh}

Grade ⟶

Cumulative Grade Distribution for a Mine Planning Increment

Figure 6.2

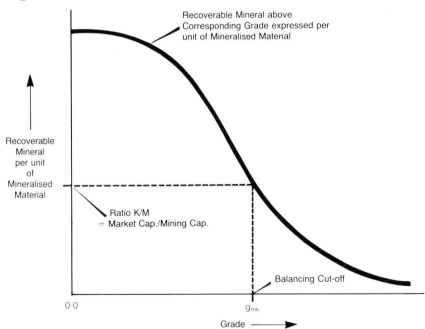

Recoverable Mineral above Corresponding Grade expressed per unit of Mineralised Material

Recoverable Mineral per unit of Mineralised Material

Ratio K/M = Market Cap./Mining Cap.

Balancing Cut-off

0·0

g_{mk}

Grade ⟶

Recoverable Mineral per unit of Mineralised Material as a function of Grade

Figure 6.3

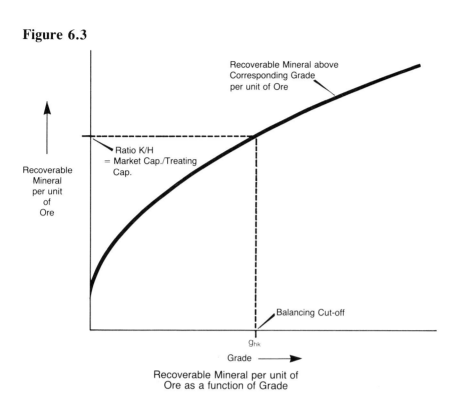

Recoverable Mineral above Corresponding Grade per unit of Ore

Recoverable Mineral per unit of Ore

Ratio K/H = Market Cap./Treating Cap.

Balancing Cut-off

g_{hk}

Grade ⟶

Recoverable Mineral per unit of Ore as a function of Grade

mineral content. The latter will increase as the grade limit increases.) If the market capacity is K units per year, then the market and the mine will balance when the recoverable mineral per unit mined equals the ratio K/M. This is at the mine/market balancing cut-off grade, g_{mk}, which is also shown in figure 6.2.

The graph of the ratio of the mineral content to the proportion of mineralised material above a range of grade limits is effectively a graph of average head grades. The difference is the incorporation of a recovery factor. In this case, as mentioned in the previous paragraph, the graph increases steadily as in figure 6.3. When the graph attains the ratio K/H, the treatment plant and the market are in balance and the corresponding grade at which this occurs is the treatment plant/market balancing cut-off grade, g_{kh}.

The determination of the balancing cut-off grades in a particular case is best achieved in practice by tabulating the grade distribution data for the relevant mine planning increment and extending it with columns of ratios and cumulative values. The balancing points can then frequently be found by inspection. The detailed calculations are illustrated by the example included in Case Study 3 (p.116).

Mines operating with more than one component of the system at capacity are the rule rather than the exception. Most mine operators appreciate that idle capacity usually involves some cost so, as far as possible, plans are moulded to exploit fully the capacities available. Should this prove difficult in the course of time, capital proposals to expand the restricting component are frequently prepared and commonly implemented because of the advantages which arise from eliminating a bottleneck at a marginal capital cost.

The role of cut-off as a balancing parameter is, in effect, understood but not usually admitted. The reason seems to be that cut-off is regarded, rightly, as a strategic parameter and, as a consequence, managements are reluctant to use it for tactical purposes. Instead, plans are reworked, including or excluding doubtful ore as necessary, until a satisfactory balance has been obtained. This amounts to changing the cut-off grade even though it is not acknowledged.

Balancing cut-off grades actually have both strategic and tactical elements. The strategy is the average level which achieves a balance in the longer term. The tactics are the week-to-week or the month-to-month changes which are found necessary to accommodate the shorter term variations in the mineralised material which is available for mining. One function of mine planning is to develop plans which iron out such short-term variations in the interest of smooth efficient running of the mine, but mineralised bodies are not always amenable. In other words, balancing cut-off grades are dynamic parameters which are dependent upon the grade distribution of the mineralised material that is available for mining at any point in time.

CHAPTER SEVEN

Effective Optimum Cut-Off Grades

The quest for an optimum has led to a plethora of cut-off grades — six, in fact. There are three limiting economic cut-off grades and three balancing cut-off grades corresponding to the three possible pairings of the limiting components of the mining system.

The multiplicity of contenders for the title of effective optimum is, of course, a consequence of the form of the economic model. It gives rise to six different possibilities, but only one of them is feasible under any given set of operating conditions. Frequently, the feasible possibility is apparent from the structure of the application, but this is not always the case and a logical procedure for identifying the right one is required.

The best way to examine the interrelations of the six cut-offs is to calculate the variable v which was introduced in Chapter 5. This variable v is actually the rate of change of V^*, the optimum present value, with respect to resource usage (dV^*/dR). In other words, it is the increment in present value per unit of resource utilised. It has to be maximised in order to determine the optimum cut-off grade. The formula is

$$v = (p-k)xy\bar{g}-xh-m-(f+F)\tau$$

v takes three forms according to the determinant of τ

$$v_m = (p-k)xy\bar{g}-xh-m-(f+F)/M$$
$$v_h = (p-k)xy\bar{g}-x\{h+(f+F)/H\}-m$$
$$v_k = \{p-k-(f+F)/K\}xy\bar{g}-xh-m$$

The graphs of all three forms of v as a function of the cut-off grade, g,

Figure 7.1

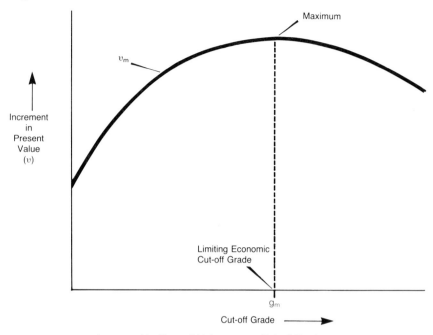

Increment in Present Value versus Cut-off Grade
Single Component (M); Limiting Economic Optimum

Figure 7.2

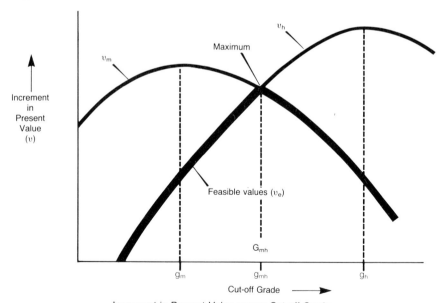

Increment in Present Value versus Cut-off Grade
Two Components (M & H); Balancing Optimum

are similar; convex upwards with a single maximum. This maximum corresponds to the limiting economic cut-off grade for the component concerned. This is illustrated in figure 7.1. If the graphs for two forms of v are superimposed, then the picture is as shown in figure 7.2. The two forms in this case correspond to the mine and the treatment plant. The intersection of these two graphs is given by

$$v_m = v_h$$

which reduces to

$$x = H/M$$

This means that the point of intersection corresponds to the balancing cut-off grade, g_{mh}. Further, it can easily be shown from the formulae that for values of cut-off less than g_{mh} the treatment component is limiting and that for values above g_{mh} the mining component is limiting. In other words, the feasible form of v, at any cut-off grade, is always the lower of the two curves. It is shown as a bold line in figure 7.2. The maximum feasible value of v in the figure occurs at the point of intersection, g_{mh}. However, this is not always so and two other cases must also be examined. These, too, are best illustrated graphically and are shown in figures 7.3 and 7.4 presented overleaf.

Figure 7.3 shows that when the balancing cut-off grade g_{mh} is less than g_m, the mine is really the bottleneck in the operation and g_m is the optimum cut-off grade. On the other hand, as figure 7.4 shows, when g_{mh} is greater than g_h, the treatment plant is the bottleneck and g_h is the optimum cut-off grade.

Thus, the following rule may be formulated for an operation limited by the mine and treatment plant. The effective optimum cut-off grade is called G_{mh}.

Mine and Treatment Plant

$$\begin{aligned} G_{mh} &= g_m \quad \text{if } g_{mh} < g_m \\ &= g_h \quad \text{if } g_{mh} > g_h \\ &= g_{mh} \quad \text{otherwise.} \end{aligned}$$

In a similar way, by considering the other pairs of stages:

41

Figure 7.3

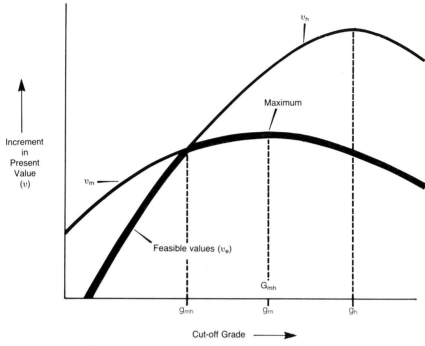

Increment
in
Present
Value
(v)

v_h

Maximum

v_m

Feasible values (v_e)

G_{mh}

g_{mh} g_m g_h

Cut-off Grade

Increment in Present Value versus Cut-off Grade
Two Components (M & H); M Limiting Optimum

Figure 7.4

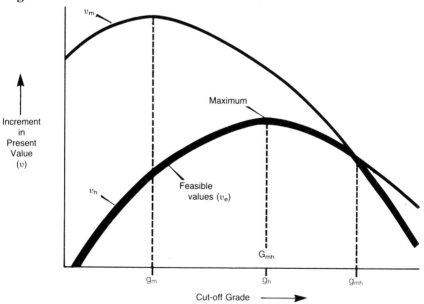

v_m

Increment
in
Present
Value
(v)

Maximum

v_h

Feasible
values (v_e)

G_{mh}

g_m g_h g_{mh}

Cut-off Grade

Increment in Present Value versus Cut-off Grade
Two Components (M & H); H Limiting Optimum

Mine and Market

$$G_{mk} = g_m \quad \text{if } g_{mk} < g_m$$
$$= g_k \quad \text{if } g_{mk} > g_k$$
$$= g_{mk} \quad \text{otherwise.}$$

Treatment Plant and Market

$$G_{hk} = g_k \quad \text{if } g_{hk} < g_k$$
$$= g_h \quad \text{if } g_{hk} > g_h$$
$$= g_{hk} \quad \text{otherwise.}$$

The overall effective optimum cut-off grade is now one of the three, G_{mh}, G_{mk} and G_{hk}. The position can again be illustrated graphically, as in figure 7.5 overleaf.

The largest increase in present value that can be achieved at any cut-off grade, allowing for the capacity restrictions, is actually the least of v_m, v_k and v_h. This is represented by the three curved segments shown by the bold line in figure 7.5. The optimum cut-off grade obviously corresponds to the highest point on these segments and it can be shown that it always occurs at the middle value of G_{mk}, G_{mh} and G_{hk}.

i.e. Effective Optimum Cut-Off Grade G
$$= \text{Middle Value } (G_{mk}, G_{mh}, G_{hk})$$

In the case illustrated in figure 7.5, it is G_{mk}. Further, the associated increase in present value v is always the least of the three increases which are possible considering the stages in pairs. The latter result is obvious; it cannot be possible that the imposition of a third restriction on capacity improves the position. The former result becomes apparent from enumerating the possibilities.

The highest point on the three segments need not be at one of the vertices as in the diagram. Depending on the relative positions of the three incremental present value curves, it can be at one of the maximum points at g_m, g_k or g_h. Under these circumstances, total capacity is limited by the one stage only and two of the associated values of G_{mh}, G_{mk} and G_{hk} coincide. Figure 7.6 illustrates this position. Here G_{mh} and G_{hk} coincide at g_h. This is the effective

Figure 7.5

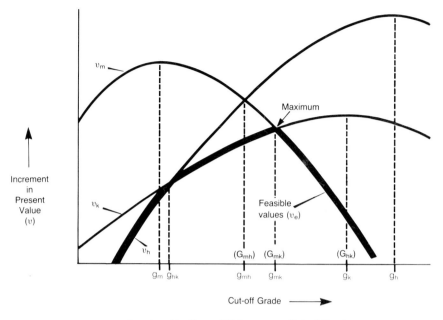

Increment in Present Value versus Cut-off Grade
Three Components; Separate Paired Maxima

Figure 7.6

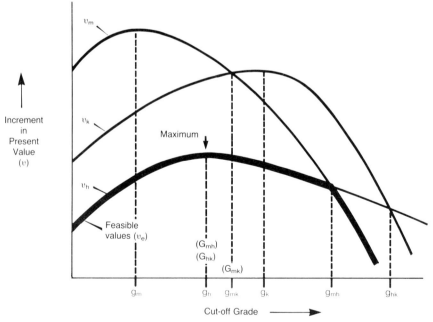

Increment in Present Value versus Cut-off Grade
Three Components; Two Paired Maxima Coincident

optimum and the treatment plant alone limits capacity. Case Study 3 illustrates the application of these ideas.

The method of first determining limiting economic cut-off grades and then balancing cut-off grades in order to arrive at an effective optimum cut-off has been described in detail because of the insight it gives into the factors which influence the optimum. Other more direct methods can be employed and are sometimes necessary, as when the maxima of the economic model cannot be located by simple means. One alternative method, a search technique, has already been mentioned. It is described in Chapter 11.

CHAPTER EIGHT

Economic Forecasts

Previous chapters have shown that the economic definition of ore is dependent upon the current values of prices, costs and performances, and upon two terms which are influenced by the future values of these parameters. The two terms are the present value of the operation and the rate of change of this present value with time.

If the purpose of the analysis is confined to determining the current optimum cut-off grade, then only the current values for these two terms are required. As both can only be rough estimates, dependent as they are on future projections, any reasonable method of approximation may be employed to obtain satisfactory values.

In the larger companies there may be an economist with responsibility for establishing short- and long-term price forecasts. There may also be a planning department which monitors costs and performances against a budget: the department may even have a rolling five-year plan for longer term planning. These figures should be taken as the basis for present value estimation, extending into the future by repeating the last year, or the average of the last three years, or whatever is considered to be a typical year.

It is usually simplest and most satisfactory to assume stable prices and costs beyond a certain time horizon. However, some companies have a policy of escalating estimates and it is important to have consistency between cut-off policies in related areas so, in such cases, the escalation should be included. The remaining life of the operation is usually well known, if not well publicised.

Not uncommonly, the future beyond a certain time is too uncertain to justify any detailed estimation. Minerals in over-supply, but currently sold under fixed contracts, are examples. In these circumstances, the equivalent of a directors' valuation may be the best figure to use, if one can be obtained. This is assumed to be so in Case Study 3. (It is, of course, always possible to take several values to see whether the assumption has much effect on cut-off.) Sometimes a recent present value estimate will already have been made for some other purpose. For example, a bank submission for additional finance would usually require a valuation; so, too, would a re-appraisal of company worth for a deal of some kind. This is illustrated in Case Study 2.

Estimating the rate of change of present value with time requires a second present value estimate, namely the present value as it would be in a year's time if the reserves were to remain the same. It is impracticable and unrealistic to make complicated assumptions about this term. Generally, the only kind of forecast which can be made with any confidence involves just one significant price movement. For example, the current price may be considered to be low and the forecast might envisage an increase at some time in the future to a stable, long-term level. The impact of such a forecast on present value can be calculated by an adjustment to the first year; the present value in a year's time is the same as the present value now except for the loss or gain of revenue as a consequence of the price movement. In fact, for more complex price and cost assumptions it is still often possible to obtain good enough estimates of the present value a year hence by suitable adjustments to the present value now. This is illustrated in Case Studies 2 and 3.

For less sophisticated applications, the problems of forecasting and estimating are usually simpler because there is not the same established framework of conventions and procedures to be followed. A typical annual cash flow can be ascertained and taken as constant for the future. Discount tables give a present value estimate and a single adjustment for a price movement gives a modified estimate for one year hence. This is the technique employed in Case Study 4.

However, if a more ambitious analysis is being undertaken, say to determine a complete cut-off policy for the rest of the mine's life, then estimates of the present value terms are required for each year involved and obviously these estimates must be consistent with one another. This means that detailed price, cost and performance data must be available for every year. So, also, must data on the availability of mineralised material. These data are used as a basis for calculating annual cash flows which, in turn, provide present value estimates. This is an elaborate procedure, not least because the cash flows are dependent upon cut-off grades which are themselves dependent upon the present values. This problem has already been mentioned in Chapter 3. The apparent circle can be broken by a mathematical technique of successive approximations which is described in Chapter 10.

A complete cut-off policy is instructive, even though composed only of estimates, and estimates of increasing uncertainty as they go further into the future. It reveals the factors which may influence cut-off at different times and it shows trends. It is therefore valuable for future planning and is particularly important during the feasibility study and early development stages of a new operation. Complete cut-off policies are calculated in Case Studies 4, 6 and 7.

One other economic parameter is important, the cost of capital or discount rate. Again, in the larger companies figures are likely to be readily available and the only question may be which figure is appropriate for the purpose. In smaller companies this is less likely to be the case. As a rough guide, a figure of 7% after tax or 14% before tax is commonly accepted. Cut-off analyses are nearly always undertaken before tax because tax tends to be a complex and specialised subject; thus, the larger figure is the more relevant. With an added allowance for risk, the discount rate is usually taken to be between 15% and 20%.

The discount rate is a parameter which can be varied in order to change the objective of the optimisation in particular circumstances. For example, a discount rate of 0% will maximise the total cash flow from the operation. By contrast, a very high discount rate will maximise the short-term cash flow. There can be tactical reasons for adopting modified objectives of this kind.

CHAPTER NINE

Mineralised Reserve Estimates

In general, the determination of effective optimum cut-off grades requires information about the grade distribution of the mineralised material which is available for mining. As is the case with present value estimation, this is a comparatively easy requirement to meet if the purpose of the analysis is confined to determining only the current optimum cut-off grade; it is much more difficult and complex if the purpose is to determine an optimum cut-off policy for several years.

The whole subject of long-term reserve estimation is a huge one which has received a lot of attention within the industry for many years. Many books have been written about it and the science of geostatistics has provided a theoretical foundation for much of the recent work which was lacking earlier. Nevertheless, reserve estimation retains a large element of art and each deposit tends to have its own unique features which are only understood gradually as experience of the deposit is acquired. Overall the subject is beyond the scope of this book, but certain aspects are particularly important in relation to cut-off grade determinations.

Normal and prudent practice is to have at least several months' supply of potential ore developed and available for mining at all times. Usually this material has been well sampled and quite detailed information is on record concerning tonnage and grades. This information is necessary for short-term mine planning purposes and the same information is required for the calculation of balancing cut-off grades as described in Chapter 6. It is usually sufficient for the determination of a current optimum cut-off as is illustrated in the first four Case Studies. Beyond this, however, the amount of information on record about potential ore in the more distant future varies very much from one property to another. Some are regular and consistent mineralised bodies so that the spectrum of available grades changes little from year to year; certain sedimentary gold mines are examples. Other mines are of such size and significance that extensive drilling programmes have been undertaken and detailed long-range plans have been developed in order to ensure that production can continue at satisfactory levels into the future; large porphyry copper mines are examples. Yet other mines are on complex deposits whose continuity and structure are difficult to predict; many of the smaller vein-type deposits are in this category.

Whatever the nature of the mineralisation, however, the determination of a cut-off policy for years in the future cannot be undertaken without some description of the grade distributions that are likely to be encountered during the years concerned. This means either long-range mine plans for the period or some statistical basis for extrapolating from present and past results.

Of course, no mine plans can be drawn up without some prior assumptions about cut-off grades, but this is more of an apparent theoretical problem than a real practical difficulty. Mine planning is a process of working and reworking data and it is possible to take any sensible starting values and then to refine them repeatedly until the plans are acceptable. (This usually means repeating them until there is no apparent way to achieve any further improvements.) Cut-off grades are just one element in this process which is concerned with the whole problem of the optimum progression through the mineralised body.

Plans are naturally less reliable the further they extend into the future, but the effect of discounting diminishes the consequences of this on current cut-off values. Detailed plans for the first two or three years are important and so too are approximate plans for the next five years or so but, beyond that, fairly crude figures are usually good enough.

The mineralised reserve figures that are required for a cut-off analysis are estimates of tonnages and grades that will be achieved as a consequence of working to different operational cut-off values. The crucial word here is 'operational'. Two considerations are especially important.

The first is selectivity. Different mining methods achieve different degrees of selectivity between ore and waste. For example, small shovels and trucks can discriminate between ore and waste on a finer basis than large ones. Similarly, underground, small-scale open stopes give rise to less dilution than large-scale block caving methods. The grade distribution data must, therefore, be related to the actual degree of selectivity that is practicable with the equipment that is in use. Geostatistics provides a basis for modifying distributions to allow for different sizes of mining units.

The second is the accuracy of grade measurements for grade control. Because sampling and assaying involves statistical errors, some material will be mis-classified; ore will be rejected as waste and vice versa. This effect is examined in some detail in Chapter 12. Where reasonably possible it should also be integrated into the grade distribution data. In other words, the grade distribution should consist of estimates of the tonnages and grades that will be achieved by operating at the different cut-off grades regardless of the actual occurrence of the different grades in the mineralised body.

Generally, the effect of both poor selectivity and poor grade measurements for grade control is to yield more ore at a lower grade than predicted. Unfortunately, this is a commonplace feature of many mines.

A popular misconception in relation to mineralised reserves is that the cut-off directly determines which parts of a mineralised body should be mined. The presumption is that any part of the body above cut-off should be identified as ore. This interpretation is not always correct. To recapitulate, cut-off is an operational criterion which is applied at the point of mining. Whether or not a particular area should be mined at all is a question which can only be answered by a separate economic analysis which takes into account the average grade of any mineralised material above cut-off and weighs it against the additional costs. For example, material within an established ultimate open pit will be mined and treated as ore if it is above the current cut-off at the time of mining. However, material above cut-off in the wall would only be mined if it could be shown that the average grade and tonnage of such material would at least repay the cost of the additional stripping. If this were so, the ultimate pit would be redefined to include the additional material. This should have been the basis on which the ultimate pit was determined in the first place. Similarly, a cut-off underground only determines whether a panel or stope is mined once it has been developed. Whether or not it is worth developing can only be decided by an economic analysis of the cost of developing and mining versus the average grade and tonnage within the stope.

It is convenient to present reserve data in the form of a table giving grade categories along one side and mining increments along the other. (Specimen tables for a single increment are included in Case Studies 3, 4 and 5.) The increments correspond to successive phases of the mine plan and can be of whatever size conforms to normal mine planning practice. For example, if mine plans are projected in some detail for four quarters, then more approximately each year for several years and, finally, very roughly in five year periods, these same phases should be adopted for mining increments in the table. However, it is important that mining increments are defined in terms of tonnage, not time. Although the increments may correspond approximately to quarters or years, they are not linked to these periods and different cut-off strategies will cause them to be mined at different rates. In fact it is good, although not common mine planning practice, to work in tonnages for as long as possible and to avoid making premature conversions to time intervals. Plans should be drawn up for mining the next, say, 1 million tonnes, leaving open the question of whether this might take 11, 12 or 13 months, or some other period. Similarly, the grade categories can be taken to correspond with the categories normally used for grade analyses.

A minor point is the regularity of the grade intervals; if they are irregular the arithmetic of interpolation becomes complicated and it can prove easier to re-estimate the tonnages in regular intervals from the beginning.

A major point is the consistency of the grade data with the category limits. Consistency, in this context, means that the average grades within each category conform to reasonable assumptions about the distribution of grades between the category limits. The point may be illustrated by considering the very much simplified grade tonnage reserves presented in Table 9.1. This table is typical in form but with rounded tonnages and only four categories.

Table 9.1

Grade Category (% Cu)	Tonnage (10^3 tonnes)	Average Grade (% Cu)	Contained Cu (tonnes)
0-0·200	30·0	—	—
0·201-0·300	40·0	0·250	100
0·301-0·400	50·0	0·380	190
0·401+	100·0	0·650	650

The common assumption, when interpolating such a table of reserves, is that the average grades apply uniformly within each category. Thus, the tonnage and grade above, say, 0·30% Cu is 840 tonnes contained copper in 150,000 tonnes, i.e. 0·56%; or, above say 0·35% is 745 tonnes (650 tonnes plus half of 190 tonnes) in 125,000 tonnes, i.e. 0·596%. Any cut-off grade based upon such interpolations is likely to be misleading because it will indicate that the incremental ore created by reducing the cut-off grade from 0·35% to 0·30% is 25,000 tonnes at a grade of 0·38%. This is an inconsistency because the average grade, by definition, should be between the two cut-off limits.

The problem can sometimes be circumvented by an alternative assumption about the distribution of grades within the categories.

For example, within the second category the distribution could be assumed to be rectangular. This would give rise to an average at the mid point, 0·25%, which is consistent with the actual average as shown in figure 9.1. Otherwise, if the actual average is near the middle value but not equal to it, a trapezoidal distribution could be assumed as shown in figure 9.2. In the case illustrated, more material is assumed to be at the upper end of the category than the lower end and, as a result, the average grade exceeds the mid-value. If the

Figure 9.1

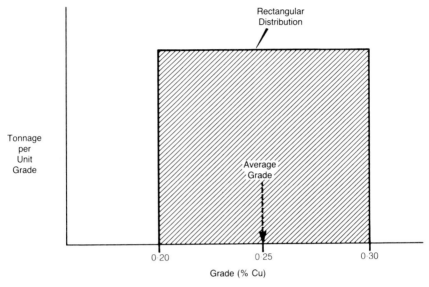

Rectangular Distribution of Grades
within a Grade Category

Figure 9.2

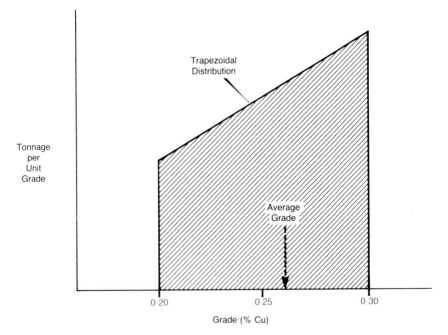

Trapezoidal Distribution of Grades
within a Grade Category

opposite had been assumed then the average grade would have been lower than the mid-value.

The formulae for the trapezoidal interpolation of tonnages and grades above a grade g within an interval (g_1, g_2) when the average is $\bar{g}$ are

$$\text{Tonnage} = \Pi(g_2-g)\,[3g(2\bar{g}-g_1-g_2)$$
$$+ g_2(g_2+g_1) - 2g_1(3\bar{g}-2g_1)] / (g_2-g_1)^3$$
$$\text{Mineral} = \Pi(g_2-g)\,[2g^2(2\bar{g}-g_1-g_2)$$
$$+ (g+g_2)(2g_1^2+g_2\bar{g}-3g_1\bar{g})] / (g_2-g_1)^3$$

where Π is the total tonnage in the category.

These formulae ensure consistency but can only be applied when the average grade $\bar{g}$ is less than one sixth of the grade interval from its mid-point: i.e. when it is in the central third of the interval. Outside of this range it implies a negative tonnage somewhere in the interval — an unrealistic idea. Therefore, the distribution of grades within an interval, such as the third one in the example, cannot be represented in this way (0·38 is outside the range 0·333-0·367). Of course, a distribution which is consistent with an average of 0·38 could be invented but it would be complicated and arbitrary.

In these circumstances the most practical course is to accept the existence of inconsistencies but to choose a sufficient number of grade categories to ensure that the interpolation errors are small. Something like ten covering the range to be investigated is usually more than ample.

In certain cases choosing more categories does nothing to alleviate the inconsistencies; the averages remain highly eccentric or even outside the intervals altogether. In these cases the original grades defining the categories are called parametric because they only measure the actual grades indirectly.

Parametric grades cause no fundamental problems in the analysis of cut-off grades but, as has already been mentioned in Chapter 5 the formulae quoted there for limiting economic cut-off grades are no longer directly valid and they must be adapted. Alternatively, the maximisation calculations must be performed in a different way. This is discussed further in Chapter 11 which is devoted to this subject.

CHAPTER TEN

Calculating a Complete Cut-Off Policy

Chapters 5, 6 and 7 were concerned with the calculation of the optimum cut-off grade at a single point in time. This chapter is concerned with the calculation of a sequence of optimum cut-off grades over an extended period. This constitutes what has been defined as an optimum cut-off policy.

No new principle is involved. Every cut-off grade in the sequence is an optimum cut-off grade calculated according to the principles described earlier. However, they have to be consistent in the sense described in Chapter 3; the corresponding annual cash flows and the associated sequence of present values must conform to a consistent definition of present value throughout the whole period.

In the terminology of Chapter 3, an optimum cut-off policy corresponds to a complete optimum exploitation strategy for the resource — in this case, the mineralised body. The problem is to find an exploitation track along which a consistent associated sequence of present values with a given terminal value is achieved. This is then an optimum exploitation track and the present values at every stage along it are maxima.

Usually, the period for which a policy is to be determined is the remaining life of the operation. In this case, the terminal present value is zero. It is possible to calculate a policy for a shorter period but, in such cases, a terminal present value must be specified for the resource which will remain after termination. The reason for this is that the optimisation process maximises the present value at a certain level of resource, and the maximisation formulae necessarily incorporate a value associated with continuing operations based upon any resource remaining beyond the exhaustion of the increment under study.

Obviously, the calculation of a sequence of optimum cut-off grades requires a database of information for the complete period. This means annual forecasts of the economic parameters as described in Chapter 8, and mineralised reserve estimates as in Chapter 9.

The main problem in calculating a cut-off policy as opposed to a single optimum cut-off grade is when and how to start. A tempting approach is to create the policy in reverse. Starting with the terminal value, an optimum cut-off can be calculated; hence, a cash flow for the final year and, from this in combination with the terminal value, a present value for the year prior to termination. This figure can then in turn be used for the penultimate year and the present value calculated for two years prior to termination. And so on . . .

However, there is a difficulty with this approach. The cut-off policy affects the rate of progress through the mineralised body and, until the policy has been determined, the termination time is unknown. The difficulty could be overcome by taking a series of termination times but it is more logical to start at the beginning.

The problem is then how to start because the initial levels of present value are unknown. This problem can be surmounted, however, by a mathematical iteration process. Initial levels are assumed, a policy calculated, and the present values on termination compared with the specified terminal value. Depending upon the difference, the initial levels are modified and a new policy calculated. This is a form of mathematical gunnery practice in which the direction of the gun barrel, defined by the initial levels of present value, is progressively modified until the shot is close to the target, the specified terminal value.

A complication arises from the requirement to follow two sequences of present values. As was shown in Chapter 3, the formula for determining the optimum strategy at each stage incorporates the opportunity cost term

$$F = \delta V^* - dV^*/dT$$

dV^*/dT is the rate of change of present value with time and an estimate of this term is the difference between the present value a year hence and the present value now for the same quantity of resource remaining. As a consequence, two initial levels have to be assumed and followed in two parallel streams.

Dropping the asterisks, because only on the final iteration are the present values optimum, let V_i be the present value at the beginning of year i and W_i the present value for the same resource remaining at the end of year i. Then

$$(dV/dT)_i = W_i - V_i$$
$$\text{and } F_i = \delta V_i - (dV/dT)_i$$
$$= \delta V_i + V_i - W_i$$

Using this value of F_i, the economic parameters for the period i and the mineralised reserve grades for the appropriate increment, the effective optimum cut-off grade g_i, can be determined and the corresponding cash flow c_i, calculated from the formula

$$c_i = (p_i - k_i)x_i y_i \bar{g}_i - x_i h_i - m_i - f_i$$

Occasionally a reserve increment is exhausted during a year so that another is started for the remainder of the year. In such cases the cash flow is a compound of two components calculated separately for the two increments and prorated according to the time each increment is mined. Then the next present value in the sequence can be calculated by adding interest at the cost of capital less the cash withdrawn

$$V_{i+1} = (1+\delta)V_i - c_i$$

The calculation for the W sequence is similar, but using the economic parameters for the following year. A value for W_{i+1} to form the appropriate estimate for F

$$F'_{i+1} = \delta W_i + V_{i+1} - W_{i+1}$$

is not available but $V_i - W_i$ can be taken as a first estimate of $V_{i+1} - W_{i+1}$ and another inner iteration performed to converge on W_{i+1} via the corresponding W formula

$$W_{i+1} = (1+\delta)W_i - c'_{i+1}$$

where the primes refer to the W sequence.

To keep the V and W sequences parallel, W_{i+1} must correspond to the same resource remaining as V_{i+1}. It may not be so, however, in the calculation of the preceding paragraph because of the different economic parameters and hence different optimum grades. A correction must, therefore, be applied. A simple assumption is that the W sequence is changing at the same rate with respect to resource consumed as the V sequence in the preceding year. This gives the correction

$$(r-r') \, (V_{i+1} - W_i)$$

where, as before, r is the resource consumed during the year. The modified formula for W_{i+1} becomes

$$W_{i+1} = (1+\delta)W_i - c'_{i+1} + (r-r') \, (V_{i+1} - W_i)$$

This iterative loop converges to a stable value for W_{i+1} in most practical circumstances.

The end of a policy calculation is reached when the resource is exhausted or some specified quantity remains. At this point, both the V and W sequences should be close to zero or the specified terminal value. If not, the initial levels, V_1 and W_1 must be modified and the whole calculation repeated. The process for one complete iteration is illustrated graphically in figure 10.1 overleaf.

The question of the most suitable convergence formula is a complex one depending upon the behaviour of the underlying model and the relative importance of speed and robustness (insensitivity to assumptions and small errors). However, simply applying the discounted residuals is usually effective.

If the present values on termination are V_λ and W_λ, the corresponding residuals are

$$V_\lambda - \Gamma \text{ and } W_\lambda - \Gamma$$

where Γ is the terminal value. If the corresponding life of the operation is λ years, the discounted residuals are

$$(V_\lambda - \Gamma) / (1+\delta)^\lambda \text{ and } (W_\lambda - \Gamma) / (1+\delta)^\lambda$$

These expressions are valid, even for fractional years included in λ.

Figure 10.1

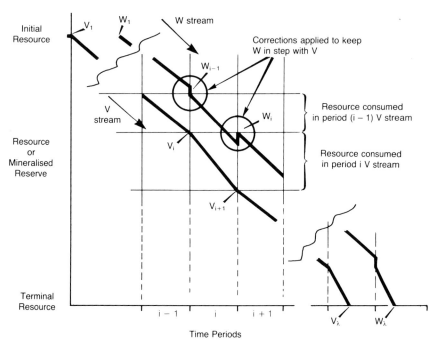

Graphical Representation of a
Single Optimum Policy Iteration

Subtracting them from V_1 and W_1 respectively gives new initial levels for another iteration.

This calculation can be elaborate and time consuming and it is best performed on a computer. It is incorporated into the OGRE (Optimum Grades for Resource Exploitation) program which is described in the Appendix (p.98). A computer system such as OGRE is a very powerful tool for studying cut-off policies. It permits the investigation of the factors which affect the policy and the way in which they influence policy over the course of time.

Illustrations of the calculation of cut-off policies are included in Case Studies 4, 6 and 7.

CHAPTER ELEVEN

Parametric Cut-Off Grades

A cut-off grade is defined as parametric if it is only indirectly related to the grade distribution of the mineralised body. Parametric cut-off grades are not at all uncommon and arise from a variety of causes including — recoveries which vary with different types of mineral, the presence of minor minerals whose equivalent values are simply added to the main mineral of the body and also to inaccuracies in grade control.

Take as an example a copper mineralised body which also contains some molybdenum. The original grade categories may well have been defined in terms of both copper and molybdenum but, because the molybdenum is only of minor importance, the complexities of a two dimensional grade analysis are avoided by calculating the copper equivalent of the molybdenum in each copper category and adding this to the copper content. A typical calculation is illustrated in Case Study 4 (p.121).

This involves a compromise between accuracy and practicability, of course. In theory, either the two dimensional grade distribution should be retained and the analysis conducted according to the methods described later in Chapter 17 or the reserve should be recompiled on the basis of the combined minerals. The latter entails adding one mineral to its equivalent of the other to form the combination at some earlier stage in the compilation of the mineralised reserve. The precise stage depends upon the method of reserve estimation: it could be the original sample stage or a later block estimate stage. In either case, recompiling the reserve is a major arithmetical exercise and, moreover, it is one which may have to be repeated should there be significant changes in the relative values of the two materials.

The alternative of combining the values in the distribution is, therefore, attractive and the approximation can be acceptable if the secondary mineral is of minor importance. The approximation can also be acceptable if the two minerals are strongly correlated one to another so that the secondary effectively only amplifies the primary mineral, or if the secondary mineral is evenly distributed throughout.

As a consequence, however, the categories of the distribution, which are defined by one mineral, are no longer directly related to the distribution itself which is based upon the combined minerals. In the example quoted earlier, the categories are still the original copper categories but the average grades are the copper equivalents of the total of the copper and the molybdenum. A cut-off grade defined in terms of the original single mineral is, therefore, one instance of a parametric cut-off grade.

The fact that a cut-off is parametric introduces no fundamental new considerations into cut-off grade theory but care has to be exercised in certain areas. In particular the distribution becomes inconsistent: if the cut-off is altered marginally, the grade of the marginal material is not necessarily near the cut-off. This invalidates the derivation of limiting economic cut-off grades given in Chapter 5.

There are two main ways to circumvent this problem. The first way is to establish a relationship between the actual distribution variable and the parametric measure. In the example this would involve finding a relationship between the copper equivalent values of the combined minerals and the original copper values themselves. Sometimes quite simple relationships can be established. For instance, in the example, if the molybdenum were randomly distributed, its effect might be to add a constant copper equivalent throughout the range. Or, if it were strongly correlated, the effect might be to add a constant percentage. Once a relationship has been established, the formulae of Chapter 5 can still be used but the cut-off grades derived must be converted, via the relationship, to the parametric measure.

The second way is to find the maxima in Chapter 5 by some technique which is insensitive to a parametric measure of cut-off grade. This alternative is perhaps less elegant but it can be more robust and better suited to calculation by computer. Recapitulating, the expression to be maximised is the incremental present value per unit of resource.

$$v = (p-k)xy\bar{g} - xh - m - (f+F)\tau$$

where τ takes one of the three forms, $1/M$, x/H, $xy\bar{g}/K$

As has been described in Chapter 7, the graph of v as a function of the cut-off grade is convex upwards with a single maximum. In practice, the cut-off grade, whether parametric or not, can only vary within a certain range so a technique is required to search this range and locate the maximum which must exist — either at one end or somewhere in between. There are many computation techniques which are suitable for this kind of application but a form of grid search has been found to be both simple and effective. Briefly, it involves calculating v at all the vertices of a coarse grid covering the range, finding the maximum, and then surrounding the maximum with a finer grid which embraces the two coarse grid intervals on either side. This process can be repeated to achieve any level of accuracy. A virtue of the technique is that it can fairly easily be extended to cover a two dimensional search as described in Chapter 16.

The result of using a search technique is that the maximum is located in terms of the parametric grade measure without reference to actual grades at all, except to the extent that they affect the calculation of the incremental present values. Any inconsistency is not, therefore, material.

Of course, if some search technique is employed to locate the limiting economic maxima it might well be extended to the location of the overall effective optimum. To do this, all three forms of v are calculated

$$v_m = (p-k)xy\bar{g} - xh - m - (f+F)/M$$
$$v_h = (p-k)xy\bar{g} - x[h + (f+F)/H] - m$$
$$v_k = [p - k - (f+F)/K]xy\bar{g} - xh - m$$

The effective limiting capacity at any cut-off is always the one corresponding to the minimum of these three. Calling it e

$$v_e = \text{Min} \ (v_m, \ v_h, \ v_k)$$

Referring again to Chapter 7, and figures 7.5 and 7.6 (p.44) in particular, the graph of v_e as a function of the cut-off grade actually consists of the curved segments shown with the bold line on these figures and referred to as feasible values. The effective optimum cut-off grade is the grade at which the maximum feasible value occurs: i.e. the grade at which v_e is maximum. Since v_e, like individual 'v's, is convex upwards, this maximum is unique and can also be found by a search process. Therefore, a single search can be used to find the overall effective optimum in one pass and it is independent of inconsistencies in the reserve data.

It is entirely possible to use a search technique in this way even in non-parametric cases. Indeed, as mentioned in Chapter 5, the form of the economic model might not permit the derivation of convenient formulae for limiting economic optima. In such cases, it may be expedient or even necessary to use a search technique. However, where possible, the methods described in Chapters 5, 6 and 7 are not only more elegant, they are usually faster.

CHAPTER TWELVE

The Effects of Inaccuracies in Grade Control

This is one of the most vexed areas in mining. It is a source of problems, some serious, in nearly every mine. Grade control is implemented on the basis of grade information derived from extensive routine sampling programmes. The method of sampling depends upon the type of mine but, across the industry, every conceivable method is employed — boreholes, blastholes, grabs, chips, channels etc. The samples are assayed and then analysed by almost every conceivable statistical technique including averaging, selecting and averaging, discounting and averaging, transforming and averaging, weighted averaging and kriging.

The problems stem from the fact that, in the end, there is usually no very satisfactory way to check the accuracy of the eventual grade predictions.

That the sampling methods are subject to large statistical variations is usually common knowledge, easily verified by a duplicate sampling programme. That the statistical techniques are dependent upon certain assumptions about the way the mineralisation varies through-out the body is usually also well understood. But the efficacy and accuracy of the whole system cannot be established without some checks between predicted and actual grades. This is the acid test but it can rarely be implemented, except as a gross average. The reason for this is that no further grade measurements are normally made until the material classified as ore is fed to the treatment plant. By that time ores from many sites in the mine have been mixed and passed through buffer stockpiles. A reconciliation is, therefore, only possi-ble over a long period such as a week or a month and then it can only

Figure 12.1

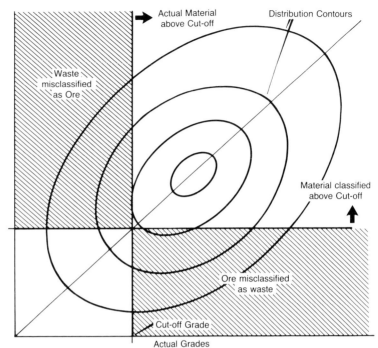

Two Dimensional Distribution of Predicted versus Actual Grades
in Minimum Mining Blocks

Figure 12.2

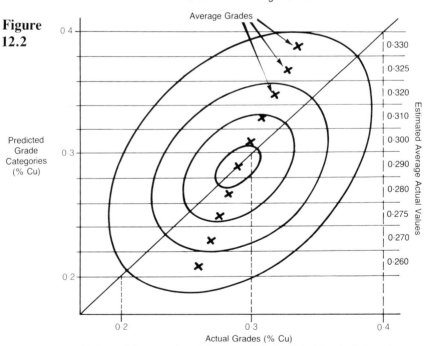

Estimated Average Actual Grades within Predicted Grade Categories
for the Distribution in Figure 12.1

confirm the consistency of average levels of prediction. This is very far from confirming that the decisions about individual mining blocks were at all satisfactory. It is quite possible that, on many mines, grade control in the sense of fine distinctions between ore and waste and careful selections of ore to achieve the right blends is largely a fiction.

However, only the distinction between ore and waste is relevant here. A mineralised body can be conceived as an assemblage of blocks that may be mined, all of the minimum size which can be mined selectively. Two statistics may be associated with each of the blocks, its actual average grade and the grade predicted by the grade control system. The formula, of course, is unknown but the two statistics (for all the blocks in a particular mine increment) form a two dimensional distribution which may be graphed as a contour map as in figure 12.1.

This distribution may be divided into categories by predicted grade intervals which form horizontal slices. Within each slice the actual section through the two dimensional distribution forms a one dimensional distribution. The average grades of these one dimensional distributions and their relative areas constitute the data that are required for the compilation of the mineralised reserve distribution estimates for the increment represented by the graph. This is illustrated in figure 12.2 which is only intended for illustration but it is possible to estimate the approximate actual average grades within the predicted grade categories by inspection.

These grades will not, in general, fall between the predicted grade limits of the interval and are, therefore, inconsistent with them. In fact, the process of averaging generally shrinks the variance and the average grades of the categories will span a narrower range than the categories themselves. For instance, in the figure 12.2, the predicted grade categories range from 0·2% to 0·4% yet the actual average grades in these categories only range from 0·26% to 0·33%. The reduction in range is one indication of the quality of the grade prediction system and a totally ineffective system would give rise to the same average grade in every category.

The predicted grades are, in fact, a parametric measure of the actual grades and a predicted grade cut-off is a parametric cut-off.

Thus, as explained in Chapter 11, the breakeven formulae for limiting economic grades must be used with caution. However, with a table such as that in figure 12.2, a conversion is easily effected. If, for example, the calculated optimum is an actual limiting economic grade of 0·27% Cu this can be seen to correspond approximately to a predicted grade cut-off of 0·22% Cu.

As nearly every mine has to base its cut-off grades on grades which are predicted in some way, the implication is that nearly all cut-off grades are parametric. Few are treated as such, however. This only matters if the mines are operating to breakeven grades but the reasons for most of the omissions are a lack of understanding of the way in which any inaccuracies in grade measurements affect the cut-off grade and a lack of sufficient reliable information about the relationship between predicted and actual grades. For the want of a better alternative, therefore, calculated cut-off grades are usually assumed to apply directly to the grade predicted by the grade control system.

For the same reason, namely the lack of reliable information, it is difficult to comment upon the significance of this assumption. It is probably an important assumption and it is certainly important to develop evidence about the accuracy of grade measurements for many other control purposes. Therefore, check sampling programmes, bulk sampling tests, analyses of historical data, geostatistical analyses and reconciliations should all be pursued in an endeavour to establish, even crudely, the form of the joint predicted and actual distribution. Its effect on cut-off policy can then be assessed.

In the case illustrated in figure 12.2, if a calculated cut-off of 0·27% Cu is applied as an operational cut-off to the predicted grades, the effect is to impose an actual cut-off of near 0·28% Cu. This difference is hardly significant. Of much more concern is likely to be the observation from the distribution that, at this cut-off, somewhere near 25% of the material is mis-classified, either ore as waste or vice versa. The grade measurements for control purposes are clearly poor. Inaccuracies present less of a problem when the optimum is a balancing cut-off. Although the calculated cut-off may be in error causing an imbalance, a balance can be effected operationally by simply making adjustments to the cut-off in practice until the balance is achieved.

An example of a parametric cut-off grade arising from inaccuracies in grade measurements and estimation is included in Case Study 5.

CHAPTER THIRTEEN

Stockpiling Intermediate Grades

An optimum cut-off grade policy commonly indicates a general decline in cut-off grades during the life of the mining operation — usually as a result of its declining present value. One implication of this phenomenon is that grades which are uneconomic to treat in the early years can be treated economically later.

The mineralised material with grades between the higher and lower cut-off grades is called intermediate grade material. Certain types of mining permit the stockpiling of such material and, in these cases, a deliberate strategy of stockpiling for later treatment can be considered. The idea has obvious attractions. In the long run, no mineralised material which can possibly be classified economically as ore at any stage during the life of the mine is rejected as waste. This maximises the amount of mineral recovered from the mineralised body, a characteristic which appeals to conservationists and property owners. At the same time, the strategy promises to improve the overall economics by increasing the cash flow in the later years when the stockpiled material is recovered.

However, the idea has its drawbacks. First, the logistics of creating a separate stockpile, or perhaps even several stockpiles if the range of intermediate grades is wide, are never easy. It will depend upon the size of the mine site and the nature of the adjacent terrain but space is always at a premium — there is the need for waste dumps, tailings areas, settling tanks, crushed ore stockpiles, water storage, maintenance facilities and even mine planning departments. An additional requirement for stockpiling intermediate grade material, which could amount to a substantial tonnage and which must be kept separate, possibly for many years, can entail redesigning much of the site layout and extending haulage routes.

Second, several additional costs are incurred. There will be the cost of longer hauls and the re-handling costs when the intermediate grade material is reclaimed. There will also be the capital cost associated with setting up the stockpiles and any ancillary equipment.

Third, the material may deteriorate during long exposure to the environment. Some leaching may occur, with a consequent loss of mineral; oxidation may create difficulties in the treatment plant and cause poor recoveries which will be another possible source of additional cost. Such effects are not always easy to anticipate because the behaviour of the material in the particular environment may not be fully understood without some years of experience.

Of course, leaching can be adopted as a deliberate secondary treatment process. It may be economically viable but it is a totally different concept to stockpiling as defined in this chapter and is not therefore discussed further here.

An optimum stockpiling policy is a complex subject. In the first place, the fact of there being a stockpile affects the cut-off equation which hitherto has been evaluated on the assumption that reject material, waste, has no value. If some goes to a stockpile from which it might be recovered economically in the future, this assumption no longer holds. In the second place, the timing of withdrawals from the stockpile is dependent, among other things, on price movements. It might, for example, be a better tactic in certain circumstances to draw lower grade material from stockpile when the price is low in order to preserve higher grade material in the mine for an expected improvement in the price at some later stage.

However, a stockpiling policy is seldom of such comparative importance that the determination of its optimum is crucial. A satisfactory compromise for most practical purposes is to calculate the mine cut-off, assigning no value to waste, and to feed stockpile material to the treatment plant when, and for as long as, the result is an increase in the cash flow.

A stockpiling policy of this kind can be evaluated by extending the mathematical model of the operation to include a stockpiling facility and calculating a complete cut-off policy for the life of the mine. Again the model should be tailored to fit the particular application; a basic model, incorporating a single stockpile to which all intermediate grade material is diverted in the early years, and from which a proportion of the mill feed is withdrawn in the later years, will reveal the essential characteristics. The additional economic parameters in the model are

s   the variable cost per tonne of recovering material from the stockpile and transporting it to the treatment plant;

y_s the recovery of intermediate grade material in the treatment process;

g_s the lower limit defining intermediate grade material.

The additional mineralised 'reserve' information is

S   the tonnage of intermediate grade material in the stockpile;

$\bar{g}_s$ the average grade of this material.

g_s is essentially a forecast of the lowest grade that can be treated economically in the conditions that will prevail when the material is recovered from the stockpile. An estimate can be obtained by assuming that the treatment plant will be limiting the throughput and that the mine will be nearing exhaustion. Under these conditions, the present value terms will be small and the lowest economic grade will be the cut-of grade given by the formula

$$g_s = (h + s + f/H)/y_s (p - k)$$

where all the parameters assume the values which have been forecast for the appropriate time. The value s appears in the formula because all material taken from the stockpile is fed to the plant as ore and therefore the recovery cost is effectively part of the ore treatment cost.

As the stockpiled material is likely to be treated well into the future, the forecast parameter values will probably have settled to stable long term levels. If not, and the timing of stockpile withdrawals is critical, an idea of the timing can be obtained from a complete cut-off policy calculated without a stockpile. A study of the pattern of grades over the years will reveal where stockpiled material could be added to the ore feed with advantage. It will also reveal the lowest grades which can be treated economically and hence provide an alternative estimate for g_s.

Once a value for g_s has been established, an algorithm for accumulating the stockpile during the calculation of a cut-off policy is elementary. After the determination of each cut-off grade g, in the sequence which constitutes the policy, the mineralised material between g_s and g is added to the stockpile, increasing the tonnage and altering the average grade.

An algorithm for withdrawals is not such an easy matter; although the principle of making a withdrawal whenever it increases the cash flow for a particular year is straightforward, the determination of the amount which maximises the cash flow for that year is not so simple. Stockpile withdrawals absorb some of the available treatment capacity and this, in turn, has repercussions on the mine cut-off.

Suppose that the amount drawn from the stockpile is q_s. Then the contribution to the annual cash flow arising from treating this material C_s is given by

$$C_s = \{(p - k)y_s\bar{g}_s - s - h\}q_s$$

The time taken to treat the material is dependent upon which of the components of the mining system is utilised longest during the treatment. If the time is t_s then

$$t_s = \max\ \{q_s/M,\ q_s/H,\ y_sg_sq_s/K\}$$

This leaves a period of $1 - t_s$, the remainder of the year, for the treatment of run of mine ore. If the quantity of mineral resource consumed is q_m, then the contribution to the cash flow from this source C_m, is given by

$$C_m = [\{(p - k)yg - h\}x - m]q_m$$

and the total cash flow C, for the year is

$$C = C_s + C_m - f$$

The formula for C_m requires a value for the optimum cut-off grade which should be applied to the run of mine material. All the results of the preceding chapters are still valid but the parameters have to be adjusted to correspond to a part year. The fixed time costs must be pro-rated according to the time available $1 - t_s$, and the capacities must be reduced by the quantities resulting from processing stockpile material. They become

$$M - q_s, \; H - q_s, \; K - y_s \bar{g}_s q_s$$

for the mine, mill and market respectively.

Thus the optimum cut-off grade g, for the run of mine material is given by

$$Max_g \; \{min \; (v_m, v_h, v_k)\}$$
$$where \; v = (p - k)y\bar{g}x - hx - (f + F)(1 - t_s)\tau$$

and v_m, v_h, v_k correspond to

$$\tau = 1/(M - q_s), \; 1/(H - q_s), \; 1/(K - y_s g_s q_s) \; respectively$$

Of course, although the formulae have been derived on the basis of feeding stockpile material for part of the year and run of mine ore for the remainder, in practice, they would be mixed.

This apparently complicated mathematical statement of the problem of stockpile withdrawals disguises a position which is much simpler in practice. The stockpile material nearly always utilises relatively more treatment plant capacity than either mine or market capacity because it is all ore and because it is low grade.

Therefore, the effect of feeding stockpile material is to lessen the relative amount of treatment plant capacity that is available for run of mine ore. As more stockpile material is added to the feed, this effect becomes more pronounced until the treatment plant component of the system becomes the limiting component for the mined ore as well as the intermediate grade ore. Beyond this stage, further stockpile material has no effect on the optimum cut-off grade calculations for the mined material so the remaining capacity must be totally absorbed by either mined ore or intermediate ore; there can no longer be a case for utilising this capacity by feeding ore partly from one source and partly from the other.

As, in the latter years of most mines' lives, the treatment plant component is already limiting with no stockpile feed, a withdrawal strategy reduces to taking 100% stockpile or 100% mined ore according to which generates more cash.

Another consideration which can eliminate unnecessary calculation is that the mine equivalent grade of the intermediate ore must exceed the cut-off grade for mined ore before there can be any basis at all for feeding stockpile material; it would be contradictory to reject material from the mine and simultaneously recover inferior material from the stockpile. The mine equivalent grade g_e is the one yielding the same marginal value at the treatment plant, i.e.

$$(p - k)yg_e = (p - k)y_sg_s - s$$
$$g_e = \{(p - k)y_sg_s - s\}/(p - k)y$$

Only when the cut-off grade for mined ore declines below g_e need stockpiling withdrawals be examined and then a detailed calculation only becomes necessary when the treatment component is not the limiting factor.

As, in practice, only stockpile withdrawals of significant quantities would be considered, a suitable algorithm is one which calculates the cash flows associated with increases in withdrawals in steps of 5% or 10% of the treatment plant capacity and selects the maximum. Not all steps have necessarily to be calculated because no change will occur at intermediate steps beyond the point where the treatment capacity is limiting throughput for both stockpile and run of mine ore.

An algorithm based upon the idea is incorporated in the OGRE program. Case Study 6 includes its application to the evaluation of a normal stockpiling proposal.

CHAPTER FOURTEEN

Planning Mine Expansions

Successful mines tend to be under constant pressure to expand. There are several reasons. First, output can generally be increased with only marginal expenditure because many of the facilities already installed are likely to be adequate to support the expansion — or nearly so. For example, access roads, housing, utilities, offices, warehouses and maintenance shops must be there to support the present mining operations.

Any increase in capacity will increase the demand on these facilities but meeting this demand will not entail expenditure comparable with a new development.

Second, the risk is far less than that associated with a new mine. The time scale is shorter, the characteristics of the mineralised body are better understood and the process is proven.

Third, the market is rarely the overriding problem that it is with other industrial activities. This observation should not be construed as meaning that markets are not a problem for the mining industry — quite the contrary. However, the structure of many markets, with international terminal exchanges, provides a certain outlet for extra production. Of course, an imbalance between supply and demand on a worldwide scale can have a disastrous affect on the price but a single development at one mine does not usually have a significant impact.

Therefore, expansion schemes are often being proposed and evaluated. A mine usually consists of several component stages and expansions can be considered in any or all of the components. A change in any capacity will generally affect the cut-off grade because of the associated changes in throughput and costs; thus any consideration of expansion proposals necessarily entails a reassessment of cut-off grade policy.

Most commonly, the proposals are to expand the ore handling and treatment facilities — the shaft, the crusher, the concentrator, the leaching circuits. This component nearly always operates at full capacity so it is an obvious candidate for expansion; however, the justification is very often on the basis that the extra capacity would permit the treatment of lower grade material which is currently dumped or left underground.

For example, consider a low grade open pit gold mine which currently operates to a cut-off of 1·20 g/tonne yielding 3 million tonnes/year of ore and 2 million tonnes/year of waste. If half of this waste grades between 0·60 and 1·20 g/tonne, it could also be treated as ore if the plant capacity were expanded to, say, 4 million tonnes/year. The figures might be

Additional revenue	$= 1 \text{ million} \times 0·9 \times 0·85 \times \$10·0$
(recovery 85% price $10·0/g	
or $311/oz)	$= \$7·65 \text{ million/year}$
Additional costs	$= 1 \text{ million} \times \$4·5$
(milling $4·5/tonne)	$= \$4·50 \text{ million/year}$
Increased cash flow	$= \underline{\$3·15 \text{ million/year}}$

This represents an attractive investment if the corresponding capital expenditure is below about $12 million.

The logic of appraisals of this kind is faultless as far as it goes but it does not go far enough. For example, in this case, if the present average grade is 2·1 g/tonne then

Present revenue	$= 3 \text{ million} \times 2·1 \times 0·85 \times 10·0$
(recovery 85% price $10·0/g	
or $311/oz)	$= \$53·55 \text{ million/year}$

If the whole operation were scaled up by one third, including the mining capacity, the cut-off grade would remain unaltered and an additional 1·67 million tonnes of material would have to be mined in order to obtain the extra 1 million tonnes of ore. The corresponding figures are:

Additional revenue	$= \$53\cdot55 \times 1/3$
	$= \$17\cdot85$ million/year
Additional cost	$= 1$ million $\times \$4\cdot5 + 1\cdot67$ million $\times \$1\cdot0$
(milling \$4·5,	
mining \$1·0/tonne)	$= \$6\cdot17$ million/year
Increased cash flow	$= \underline{\$11\cdot68 \text{ million/year}}$

Of course, the mine life will have been shortened by 25% and, therefore, the analysis is incomplete but this is an alternative expansion scheme which clearly must be assessed.

The correct form of appraisal is to make no presumption about cut-off grades at all but to specify the expansion scheme in terms of the changes in capacities and to estimate the associated capital costs. Then the optimum cut-off grade policy for the new capacities should be calculated, together with the corresponding present value. The net present value, or the difference between the present value and the capital cost, is the measure of the merit of the investment.

Generally, several alternative expansion schemes should be investigated and the results subjected to sensitivity tests with respect to the main assumptions such as price forecasts and grade estimates.

Table 14.1

	Base Case	Proposed Expansion	Alternative Expansion Schemes	
Mine Capacity (10^6 tonnes/year)	5·0	5·0	5·8	6·7
Mill Capacity (10^6 tonnes/year)	3·0	4·0	4·0	4·0
Capital Cost ($ million)	—	11·0	13·0	18·0
Incremental Present Value ($ million)	—	13·7	21·3	32·5
Incremental Net Present Value ($ million)	—	2·7	7·7	14·5
Cut-off policy (g/tonne)	1·2	0·6	0·9	1·2

Set out in Table 14.1 are possible figures for the case quoted above. These figures show that although the original proposal promised an adequate return on capital, the other possibilities are better. Of course, the case has been chosen to illustrate the point but the situation is far from rare. Pressures to reduce cut-off — from staff, mine inspectors and conservationists — have been so strong and persistent that the industry has become overmilled and undermined. Investments have been higher than necessary and the returns much lower than they could have been.

The pattern of net present values raises the question of larger capacity increases and whether or not they might yield even better returns. This is a typical position. Increases in scale nearly always yield higher returns and, eventually, a particular expansion scheme has to be selected on the basis of some other criterion such as a limitation on output or financial exposure. This is discussed further in Chapter 15.

The evaluation of expansion schemes is illustrated in Case Studies 4 and 7.

CHAPTER FIFTEEN

Designing New Mines

This chapter is concerned with the conceptual planning phase of a new mining venture. It is probably the most important in the book because the application of the cut-off theory can have more impact on the economics during early planning than at any other time in the life of a mine. It is in this phase that the main elements of an exploitation strategy are decided; it culminates in the preparation of a final feasibility study which provides the foundation for detailed engineering design.

The main elements are the method of mining, the mine plans, the scale of the operation and the cut-off grade policy. The method of mining determines the logistics of reaching and winning ore from the mineralised body. The mine plan defines the mining sequence and specifies where mining will commence and how it will progress through the mineralised body during the life of the mine. The scale of the operation is defined by the capacities of the three principal components — the mine, the treatment plant and the market. The cut-off grade policy decides which parts of the mineralised body are to be classified and treated as ore.

These elements in combination are the major determinants of the overall economics; the conceptual planning phase is therefore the most critical phase of every new mining development. It is vital that the analysis is based upon good engineering and upon sound economic principles. The differences between various exploitation strategies can be very large and the opportunity to change a strategy after construction is usually limited.

A first requirement is a description of the mineralised body. This has already been discussed in Chapter 9 but some further observations are specially relevant when the statistics are unconfirmed by any actual mining experience. The grade and tonnage data have usually to be derived from borehole samples, sometimes augmented by limited development. The general geometry of grade trends is needed for mine planning purposes and the statistical structure of grade variations is needed for predicting the effects of cut-off grade policies. A single model is not always well suited to both purposes. Block models will reveal grade trends but a simple count of blocks in different grade categories does not provide a valid means for estimating cut-off grade effects. The reason for this is that techniques for revealing grade trends are based upon moving averages in some form; they are concerned with establishing average grade levels over different regions of the mineralised body. Individual mining units will have grades that vary, perhaps substantially, from these average levels so a variance estimate is necessary for cut-off grade analyses.

For example, the predicted grades in a certain region for a tin deposit may vary from 0·15% to 0·20% Sn. If this is interpreted to mean that, at a cut-off grade of, say, 0·12% Sn the whole region will be ore, the interpretation will almost certainly prove misleading. Each mined unit will vary from the average over a range which experience suggests could be very wide, possibly from 0·0% to 0·50% Sn so that a significant proportion of the region — perhaps 25% — will prove to be waste.

How best to structure the reserve analysis to accommodate these factors remains a vexed question. The estimation variances obtained from geostatistical studies give a means for calculating the ranges of variation but their use for cut-off evaluation work is cumbersome to an impracticable degree. Disjunctive kriging gives the tonnages and grades above a specified cut-off but the technique is not widely understood and the calculations are elaborate. Many other techniques have also been developed over the years, all having application in particular circumstances.

If a limited number of comparatively homogeneous zones can be identified within the mineralised body, and a grade/tonnage curve derived for each by some means, then this forms a convenient basis for cut-off grade studies. Whatever technique is employed, though, it is still essential to allow for the inaccuracies in grade measurements for grade control purposes that will be experienced in the event. These effects have been discussed earlier.

Two further observations are particularly important for conceptual planning. First, the estimates must be based upon sound principles even if the techniques are crude: in other words, it is better to be roughly right than precisely wrong. Second, planning options must be kept open. Sometimes, for example, premature decisions about cut-off grades are taken in order to reduce the complexities of the data processing. This is a mistake because cut-off grade decisions cannot be taken until the overall economics are well understood.

On the basis of the model of the geometry of grade variations, the mining method must be determined together with a tentative mine plan, or a set of alternative plans. Often the best sequence of development through a mineralised body is not clear; starting in the richest area of mineralisation may present early marketing problems or the area may be bordered by low grades which cause temporary production difficulties.

Complete evaluations may be necessary to resolve questions of this kind. For this purpose, preliminary values have to be assumed for the scale of the operation and the associated costs. Given these, the corresponding optimum cut-off policies can be calculated. A range of possibilities should be investigated. From them, one general mine plan may emerge as superior; otherwise several may have to be carried forward for later re-evaluation when other factors have been settled. In fact, recycling in this way is typical of conceptual planning. It is an iterative process which is repeated until only minor improvements can be achieved.

The next stage in a cycle is to establish a set of scale parameters and to derive order of magnitude engineering estimates for both operating and capital costs. A range of values should be taken in order to explore the effects of component size. Optimum cut-off policies, maximum present values and net present values can then be calculated. These will indicate where attention should be concentrated in the next cycle.

The importance of a coherent cut-off theory in this process is that it permits the rapid calculation of optimum policies to maximise present values for any combination of capacities and any set of assumptions about future economic conditions. The latter is especially important because the best plan must be relatively insensitive to likely economic developments.

A good illustration of conceptual planning in practice is provided by the Bougainville open pit copper project. Although the work was undertaken nearly 20 years ago, it remains one of the best examples of early fundamental planning of this kind in the industry.

The approximate size and shape of the ultimate pit were the first factors to be established. They were modified repeatedly as more drilling data became available but they did not affect other planning factors significantly. The general characteristics of the overall mine plan were the next factors to be settled. Four principal mining sequences were identified and they were evaluated against three mine capacities and two treatment capacities; the optimum cut-off was calculated for each of the six pairings. This evaluation revealed that the highest net present values were produced consistently by one sequence — so this, with minor variations, was adopted as the basis for all further studies. These involved the evaluation of more mine and treatment plant combinations. No specific limitations were put upon the copper production but it was a factor which was taken into account in reaching final conclusions.

A computer program, an early version of the OGRE program described in the Appendix, was used to calculate the cut-off policies and the corresponding present values. The results of these evaluation studies were presented in a neat graphical form that is shown overleaf in figure 15.1.

The graph in figure 15.1 illustrates very vividly the dramatic effects of size on economics. The first estimates were for a treatment plant of 11 million tonnes/year together with a pit capacity of 18 million tonnes/year. From this beginning, the plant size was increased in three steps to 33 million tonnes, each step yielding a substantial improvement in the net present value (i.e. the difference between the present value of the cash flow and the corresponding capital costs).

Figure 15.1

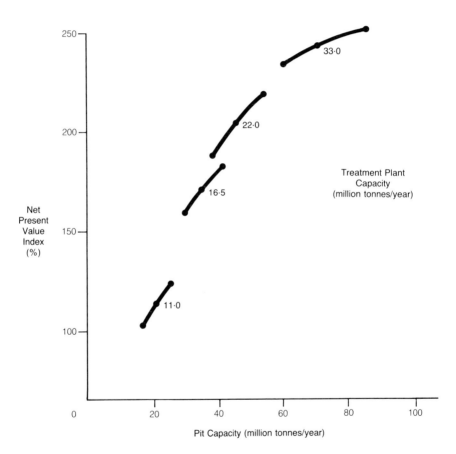

Illustration of the Effects of Pit and
Treatment Plant Capacities on Net Present Values

Then, for each plant capacity, the optimum cut-off grade policy was calculated within the constraints of a range of pit capacities determined by the size of the truck-shovel fleet and associated mining equipment. Again, the increases in capacity yielded large improvements in net present values. The combination chosen for the final design studies was 33 million tonnes/year for the treatment plant and 60 million tonnes/year for the mining equipment. This represented an improvement of over 100% in net present value over the first combination.

Although the net present value improved with increasing scale beyond this point, the risk associated with the investment became a dominant issue. The financial exposure, nearly $400 million or possibly $2,000 million in 1988 terms, was becoming very high; the world's copper supply would be suddenly and significantly increased by approximately 3%; and the sheer logistics of moving 60 million tonnes from the pit were uncertain. The management therefore judged that the apparent economic benefits of further increases in scale were offset by the added risks. Now, 15 years after the first production, the treatment plant throughput is nearly 50 million tonnes/year, about 80 million tonnes/year of material is moved from the pit and the investment has proved highly successful.

An example of conceptual planning of a new mine is included in Case Study 6 (p.135).

CHAPTER SIXTEEN

Deposits of Two Minerals

Mineralised bodies containing more than one mineral are usually dealt with by converting all the minerals to their equivalent in terms of one basic mineral, and aggregating the several values. For example, lead and zinc often occur together; assuming zinc to have twice the value of lead, the lead content can be divided by two and added to the zinc content in order to obtain a total zinc-equivalent content. Any analysis can then be conducted exactly as if the mineralisation consisted only of a single mineral.

If the minerals have fairly stable relative values, this procedure is entirely valid and it simplifies the analysis. If the relative values fluctuate, the procedure can still be valid but is often complicated because the equivalent grades have to be recalculated. If, further, one of the minerals has a restricted market for any reason, the procedure is no longer valid and the minerals must be dealt with separately.

This chapter describes the analysis for two minerals. In this case, grade distributions still exist but they are now two dimensional. Instead of a curve, a distribution is a surface and may be represented by a series of contours as presented in figure 16.1 (p88).

A cut-off is a boundary between ore and waste and it is therefore a line on this diagram. In theory, any kind of line may be considered but only straight lines are examined here. The simplest way to specify a straight line cut-off is by means of its intercepts, γ_1, and γ_2, on the grade axes. The value γ_1 is actually the cut-off grade for mineral 1 in the absence of mineral 2 and γ_2 is the cut-off grade for mineral 2 in the absence of mineral 1. The problem of determining an optimum cut-off policy for a two mineral mine is therefore the problem of determining the sequence of pairs of values for the cut-off intercepts γ_1, γ_2 which maximises the present value of the operation.

The derivation of the formulae for two minerals parallels the derivation of the single mineral formulae outlined in Chapter 5. The detail will not be repeated — only the argument. The notation is as before (p.25) but suffixes 1 and 2 are added where necessary to distinguish between the minerals.

Considering the next unit of material mined, its contribution to the net cash flow is

$$x[\bar{g}_1 y_1 (p_1 - k_1) + \bar{g}_2 y_2 (p_2 - k_2)] - xh - m - f\tau$$

where $\bar{g}_1$ and $\bar{g}_2$ are the average grades of minerals 1 and 2.

However, the quantity to be maximised is present value rather than cash flow and, as previously stated, the increment in present value is given by a similar expression but the time costs must cover the full opportunity costs, F. Thus

$$v = x[\bar{g}_1 y_1 (p_1 - k_1) + \bar{g}_2 y_2 (p_2 - k_2) - h] - m - (f+F)\tau$$

This is the basic formula and all the cut-off optima can be derived from it.

The time taken τ, to process the next unit of material is related to the constraining capacity. Four cases arise depending upon which of the four capacities — mine, mill, market (mineral 1) or market (mineral 2) — is actually limiting throughput.

Case 1   Mine Limiting, $\tau = 1/M$
$$v_m = x[\bar{g}_1 y_1 (p_1 - k_1) + \bar{g}_2 y_2 (p_2 - k_2) - h] - m - (f+F)/M$$
Case 2   Mill Limiting, $\tau = x/H$
$$v_h = x[\bar{g}_1 y_1 (p_1 - k_1) + \bar{g}_2 y_2 (p_2 - k_2) - \{h + (f+F)/H\}] - m$$
Case 3   Market 1 Limiting, $\tau = x g_1 y_1 / K_1$
$$v_{k1} = x[\bar{g}_1 y_1 (p_1 - k_1 - \{f+F\}/K_1) + \bar{g}_2 y_2 (p_2 - k_2) - h] - m$$
Case 4   Market 2 Limiting, $\tau = x \bar{g}_2 y_2 / K_2$
$$v_{k2} = x[\bar{g}_1 y_1 (p_1 - k_1) + \bar{g}_2 y_2 (p_2 - k_2 - \{f+F\}/K_2) - h] - m$$

For any pair of values γ_1, γ_2, it is possible to calculate the

Figure 16.1

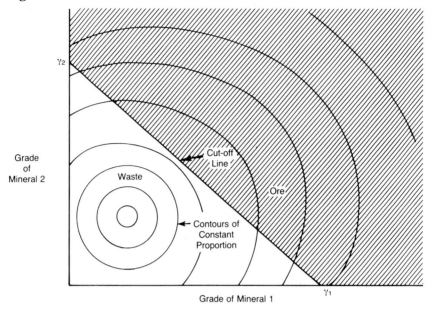

Two Dimensional Grade Distribution
for Two Minerals

Figure 16.2

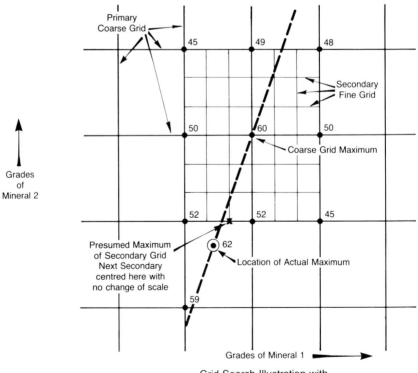

Grid Search Illustration with
Maximum Outside Secondary Grid

corresponding x, g_1 and g_2 from the appropriate two dimensional grade distribution and then to calculate v_m, v_h, v_{k1} and v_{k2}. The controlling capacity is always the one corresponding to the least of these four and, therefore it is the increment in present value resulting from the cut-off line γ_1, γ_2. It is this figure which has to be maximised. That is, maximising with respect to γ_1, γ_2

$$v(max) = Max \{Min(v_m, v_h, v_{k1}, v_{k2})\}$$

If one capacity only is dominant, the limiting economic maximisation may be accomplished analytically. For example, following a marginal tonne in Case 1, it will just contribute to the increment in present value if, when counted as ore,

$$g_1y_1(p_1-k_1) + g_2y_2(p_2-k_2) - h$$

is positive where g_1 and g_2 are the grades of the marginal tonne. Hence, the breakeven position is determined by the equation

$$g_1y_1(p_1-k_1) + g_2y_2(p_2-k_2) = h$$

This is of the form

$$g_1/\gamma_1 + g_2/\gamma_2 = 1$$

where

$$\gamma_1 = h/y_1(p_1-k_1) \text{ and } \gamma_2 = h/y_2(p_2-k_2).$$

Exactly parallel arguments follow for the other capacities giving

		γ_1	γ_2
1	Mine	$h/y_1(p_1-k_1)$	$h/y_2(p_2-k_2)$
2	Mill	$[h+(f+F)/H]/y_1(p_1-k_1)$	$[h+(f+F)/H]/y_2(p_2-k_2)$
3	Market 1	$h/y_1[p_1-k_1-(f+F)/K_1]$	$h/y_2(p_2-k_2)$
4	Market 2	$h/y_1(p_1-k_1)$	$h/y_2[p_2-k_2-(f+F)/K_2]$

These formulae are useful when a single process is limiting; however, when the maximum occurs at a balancing point, where more than one capacity restricts throughput, no satisfactory analytical technique has been developed. The problem geometrically is one of four intersecting surfaces forming hills. The peaks are comparatively easy to locate but the ridges and valleys where they intersect are more difficult. For this reason, the maximum is best located by a search process. An extension of the grid search technique, mentioned in Chapter 11, to two dimensions has been found quite effective.

This, in the two dimensional case, consists of covering the area of search with a rectangular grid, calculating the values of the function to be maximised at all of the grid points and then searching for the maximum among these points. Progressively greater accuracies are achieved by then surrounding the maximum with a finer rectangular grid over a smaller area and repeating the procedure.

In practice, it is convenient to use a primary grid of 9 × 9 cells or 100 grid points. The maximum is then overlaid by a finer grid with 6 × 6 cells or 49 grid points covering the four original cells which surround the maximum point. Finally, this step is repeated about the new maximum. This gives an accuracy of one in 9 × 3 × 3 (1 in 81) which is near 1%. It involves calculating a total of about 200 grid point values.

One safeguard has proved necessary. If the maximum occurs on the boundary of a secondary grid, the grid is relocated round the new point with no change in scale. This ensures that the maximum is still located, even when it is on a steep ridge running between grid points. In these circumstances, it is possible that it is outside the grid and further away than the dimension of one grid cell. Moving the grid, and several steps are possible, is a way of bringing the maximum back into view. The position is illustrated in figure 16.2.

When neither market is restricted, the formula for the cut-off line is of the form

$$g_1 y_1 (p_1 - k_1) + g_2 y_2 (p_2 - k_2) = \text{constant}$$

The two terms in the expression represent the 'values' of the two minerals contained in a unit of material. Therefore, the cut-off line is effectively a combined value cut-off. Indeed, as mentioned in the introduction, it is a practical and commonly adopted alternative in these cases to work in value or equivalent grade terms, thus reducing the analysis to one dimension.

When one market is restricted, additional production of the mineral concerned cannot be sold and therefore the idea of a value based on price is no longer valid. This invalidates the one dimensional combined value analysis. It also invalidates many of the other common cost versus recovery studies which are undertaken on site.

In effect, the two dimensional analysis re-assigns 'values' to the two minerals (as reflected in the parameters γ_1 and γ_2) which therefore bear a different relationship to each other. The cut-off line is tilted from its free market slope so that there is relatively more of the unrestricted mineral in the ore. The extent to which this occurs depends upon the severity of the market restriction.

A two mineral application is illustrated in Case Study 7.

CHAPTER SEVENTEEN

Other Economic Models

As explained in Chapter 4, economic models of mining operations usually have to be specially constructed for each operation but the forms generally preserve the features which have been illustrated by reference to the basic formula II (p25). Hence, in most cases, the derivation of optimum cut-off grades proceeds in a similar manner to that described for this basic case but sometimes greater complexity can be encountered. The position is illustrated in this chapter which analyses three other models which occur quite commonly. One incorporates a net-of-tax evaluation, the second incorporates a varying mill recovery and the third incorporates the effects of varying mill recoveries and throughputs simultaneously. The third model requires the application of a more sophisticated technique for determining the optimum but is otherwise equally amenable to the same cut-off theory.

Net of Tax Evaluation
Tax can be very complex and some forms of tax do, strictly speaking, invalidate the assumptions which underlie the earlier cut-off analysis. For example, if losses and depreciation can be carried forward then the assertion in Chapter 3 that the maximum present value V^*, is dependent only upon the time and the resources remaining

$$V^* = V^*(T,R)$$

is no longer true. It depends also on the level of allowances to be carried forward. However, this may prove to be only a minor point in practice and no such complication is considered in this illustration which is based on the South African tax on gold operations.

The formula for this South African tax is

$$Y = (60 - 360/X)$$

where Y is the tax payable as a percentage of the cash flow net of operating costs, lease payments and redeemable capital expenditures, and X is the same net cash flow expressed as a percentage of the revenue.

For simplicity, assume that the capital expenditure is wholly on renewals and maintenance so that it can be included in the fixed costs f. Then, using the same notation as before

$$c = (p-k)xy\bar{g} - xh - m - f\tau \quad \text{(II)}$$

and taking the treatment plant as the limiting component, $\tau = x/H$ giving

$$c = (p-k)xy\bar{g} - xh - xf/H - m$$

where c is the gross cash flow per unit of resource.

The resource utilised in a year is H/x so the corresponding annual gross cash flow is:

$$C = (p-k)y\bar{g}H - hH - f - mH/x$$

Calling the annual revenue Z

$$Z = (p-k)y\bar{g}H$$
$$X = 100C/Z \text{ (by definition in tax formula)}$$

$$\text{and Tax} = C \times Y/100$$

$$= C\{60 - 360Z/100C\}/100$$
$$= 0{\cdot}6C - 0{\cdot}036Z$$

Therefore the net of tax cash flow C′ is:

$$C' = C - \{0{\cdot}6C - 0{\cdot}036Z\}$$
$$= 0{\cdot}4C + 0{\cdot}036Z$$
$$= 0{\cdot}436(p-k)y\bar{g}H - 0{\cdot}4hH - 0{\cdot}4f - 0{\cdot}4mH/x$$

Expressed per unit of resource, again using primes

$$c' = 0 \cdot 436(p-k)xy\bar{g} - 0 \cdot 4xh - 0 \cdot 4xf/H - 0 \cdot 4m$$
$$\text{and } v' = c' - F'\tau \qquad = c' - F'x/H$$
$$= x\{0 \cdot 436(p-k)y\bar{g} - 0 \cdot 4h - (0 \cdot 4f + F')/H\} - 0 \cdot 4m$$

v' is the net of tax increment in present value which must be maximised to determine the optimum cut-off grade. It has the same structure as the expression in Chapter 5 and by the same argument as was used there the maximum occurs when

$$0 \cdot 436(p-k)y\bar{g} = 0 \cdot 4h + (0 \cdot 4f + F')/H$$
$$\text{or } g = \{0 \cdot 4h + (0 \cdot 4f + F')/H\}/0 \cdot 436(p-k)y$$

This is the net of tax (South African gold tax) equivalent of the limiting economic cut-off grade with the treatment plant limiting

$$g_h = \{h + (f+F)/H\}/(p-k)y$$

The $0 \cdot 436$ coefficient in the denominator in the net of tax formula is a consequence of the peculiar form of the S.A. tax. Had the tax been a flat 60%, the formula would be

$$g = \{0 \cdot 4h + (0 \cdot 4f + F')/H\}/0 \cdot 4(p-k)y$$
$$\text{or } g = \{h + (f + F'/0 \cdot 4)/H\}/(p-k)y$$

This is identical to the before tax formula except that the opportunity cost term F' is inflated by dividing by the complement of the tax rate $(0 \cdot 4 = 1 - 0 \cdot 6)$.

Where the tax level is 50% this term becomes $F'/0 \cdot 5 = 2F'$. As in these circumstances the net of tax cost of capital will be half the before tax figure, commonly 7% and 14%, the two terms, ignoring the dV^*/dt component, will be approximately the same multiple of the present value.

$$\text{i.e. } F'/0 \cdot 5 = 0 \cdot 07V'/0 \cdot 5 = 0 \cdot 14V'$$
$$\text{and } F = 0 \cdot 14V$$

In the longer term the before and after tax present values should be similar ($V' = V$) so that the two formulae will give similar results for the optimum cut-off grade. This is the justification for working gross

94

of tax at double the net cost of capital as an acceptable approximation in most cases. An after tax evaluation is illustrated in Case Study 5.

Varying Mill Recovery
Mill recovery often depends upon the grade of the feed material and the relation can take many forms. One common form can be represented by the formula

$$y = Y(\bar{g}-\gamma)/\bar{g}$$

This implies a fixed level of tailings loss γ with, above this, a recovery which improves with head grade towards Y.

Typical figures for a low grade copper ore might be

$$\gamma = 0.025\% \text{ and } Y = 0.90 \ (90\%)$$

At a head grade of 0.5% this formula gives

$$y = (0.5 - 0.025) \times 0.9/0.5$$
$$= 0.855 \ (85.5\%)$$

Substituting the formula in expression II

$$c = (p-k)xY(\bar{g}-\gamma) - xh - m - f\tau$$
$$= (p-k)xY\bar{g} - x\{(p-k)Y\gamma + h\} - m - f\tau$$

This is the same form as expression II but with a different coefficient; instead of h there is the term $(p-k)Y\gamma + h$. Thus all the earlier analysis still applies but the treatment cost must be inflated by the addition of the term $(p-k)Y\gamma$ which is actually a measure of the inherent value of the tailings.

Varying Mill Recovery and Throughput
Referring again to the basic formula II with the treatment plant limiting

$$v = (p-k)xy\bar{g} - xh - x(f+F)/H - m$$

It has so far been assumed, when maximising this expression, that

95

only x and g vary and that both are simply dependent upon the cut-off grade. Much more complicated assumptions are possible. The maximisation is then also more complicated but still feasible.

For example, it is often the case that the recovery in the mill is dependent upon the feed grade which, in turn, is dependent upon the cut-off.

$$y = y(\bar{g}) \qquad = y(g)$$

An example of this was the subject of the previous section. In addition though, the mill may have a designed capacity of $\bar{H}$ but the feed rate may, in practice, be varied with some consequent gain or loss in recovery

$$y = y(H)$$

combining these two effects

$$y = y(g, H)$$
$$\text{and } v = (p-k)xy\bar{g} - xh - x(f+F)/H - m$$

is a function of the two variables g and H.

An expression of this kind can be maximised by finding the stationary points

$$\delta v/\delta g = \delta v/\delta H = 0$$

If $\phi(z)$ is the grade distribution function

$$x = \int_g^\infty \phi(z)dz \qquad x = \int_g^\infty \bar{g}\phi(z)dz$$

Then $\delta v/\delta g = (p-k)[x\bar{g}\delta y/\delta g - yg\phi(g)] + \phi(g) \{h + (f+F)/H\}$

$$\text{and } \delta v/\delta H = (p-k)x\bar{g}\delta y/\delta H + x(f+F)/H^2$$

Putting these two expressions equal to zero and rearranging:

$$g = \{h + (f+F)/H\}/(p-k)y + (\delta y/\delta g)x\bar{g}/y\phi$$
$$\text{and } 0 = (p-k)XG\delta y/\delta H + x(f+F)/H^2$$

The first of these equations shows that the cut-off grade is the same as before but with an added term related to the rate of change of recovery with grade. Equations of this kind can be solved by numerical methods which are readily adaptable to computer applications. They have been studied in some detail by Wouter Schaap whose papers are included in the references. However, it is not the intention of this chapter to pursue such complexities but only to show that the theory is still valid.

OGRE — Optimum Grades for Resource Exploitation

The OGRE program was developed by RTZ Consultants for assignment applications. It is essentially a sophisticated mine planning tool.

The calculation of a single optimum cut-off grade for one particular set of conditions is not difficult. Even when present value terms have to be estimated, the arithmetic is still well within the capability of a hand calculator. The calculation of a complete cut-off policy, however, is a different matter; a sequence of cut-off grades for the life of the mine has to be calculated and, further, the sequence has to be consistent in that the corresponding annual cash flows and present values must relate consistently to each cut-off grade in the sequence.

Complete cut-off policies are not a normal requirement for day-to-day mining operations, but they are important for longer range mine planning. Future cut-off grades affect development requirements, equipment utilisation and output. They also affect the future cash flow — the resource which underlies all planning.

Beyond this, projects to expand or improve performances imply a change in cut-off policies, and pre-feasibility studies entail the comparison of many alternative plans, each with associated cut-off policies, which have to be evaluated for a range of different conditions.

OGRE is designed as an aid to this kind of planning. A mining operation is defined by a set of capacities, costs, recoveries and prices — all of which can be varied according to time or tonnage. The mineralised reserves are described by grade/tonnage tables in increments corresponding to the mine plans. The program calculates the optimum cut-off policy for a particular combination of these parameters and prints a comprehensive set of tables giving the corresponding production, cash flows and present values. Once set up, parameter values are easily changed and policies rapidly re-evaluated.

The original version of OGRE was written nearly 20 years ago to assist with the planning of several large-scale open pit mines. Since then it has been substantially improved and extended and has been applied to many operations under a wide variety of circumstances. The present version of the program is fairly general. It incorporates both single and two mineral variants, and stockpiling is an option. Past versions have included a contaminating mineral which increases processing costs and a multi-stage upgrading plant. These and others are optional but are not incorporated in the standard program because they are considered to be too specialised.

The program is written in FORTRAN and consequently is easily transported to most machines with a FORTRAN compiler. There is a PC version: most applications will run on it in a matter of minutes but the stockpile option takes longer and the two mineral version can take up to an hour.

Summary of Routines

The routines which constitute the OGRE program are of two kinds: optimisation and housekeeping. The optimisation routines are the core of the system; three are important.

One calculates the optimum cut-off grades according to the present theory. It requires information on costs, prices, recoveries, capacities and present values at each stage of the operation.

Another determines optimum stockpile withdrawals. It does this by incrementing withdrawals and working in tandem with the optimum cut-off grade routines until the cash flow at each stage is a maximum.

The third integrates the stages to obtain the present value for the complete operation and then iterates through the whole sequence until a maximum present value is reached. In order to measure the

Figure A.1

PROGRAM LOGIC DIAGRAM

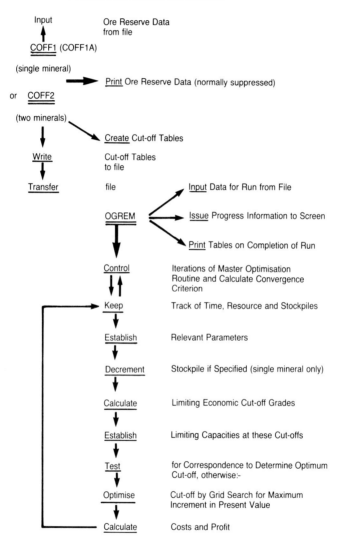

Input ↑ COFF1 (COFF1A)	Ore Reserve Data from file
(single mineral)	
	Print Ore Reserve Data (normally suppressed)
or COFF2	
(two minerals) ↓	
	Create Cut-off Tables
Write ↓	Cut-off Tables to file
Transfer	file
OGREM	Input Data for Run from File
	Issue Progress Information to Screen
	Print Tables on Completion of Run
Control	Iterations of Master Optimisation Routine and Calculate Convergence Criterion
Keep	Track of Time, Resource and Stockpiles
Establish	Relevant Parameters
Decrement	Stockpile if Specified (single mineral only)
Calculate	Limiting Economic Cut-off Grades
Establish	Limiting Capacities at these Cut-offs
Test	for Correspondence to Determine Optimum Cut-off, otherwise:-
Optimise	Cut-off by Grid Search for Maximum Increment in Present Value
Calculate	Costs and Profit

effects of varying economic parameters, it actually maintains two parallel sets of calculations separated by a single period of time.

The housekeeping routines are manifold. There are 20 parameters, each of which can assume up to 60 values. Their input has to be effected, and account has to be kept of them during the course of each iteration through the life of the operation.

Four stockpiles are permitted and their status has to be maintained throughout, a complex requirement particularly during trial optimisation calculations.

Ore reserves and mine plans are described by grade tonnage distributions in mine increments. In total, 50 increments are permitted with up to 30 × 20 grade cells in each for a two mineral reserve.

In addition, production and accounting schedules have to be compiled and recorded. (There is a limit of 100 periods on the life of the operation.) Then they have to be marshalled into tables for output.

In total, there are about 4,000 lines of FORTRAN code, organised into 75 modules. These, in turn, are grouped into 10 files which correspond to distinct separable functions.

The structure of the program, and the interrelationship of the modules, is illustrated in the program logic diagram (figure A.1).

Operation of the Program

This is illustrated with a specimen run. Two input files must be prepared, one giving the ore reserve tonnages in grade intervals by mine increments and the other giving the control parameters and the operating data.

The first file is processed by a preliminary program, called COFF, the purpose of which is to convert the tonnage grade data into a cut-off table form which is more efficient for subsequent calculations. This preliminary processing need only be effected once for a given set of data; if the reserve data are altered, then COFF must be re-run.

The second file controls the main program and sets the values for the operating data for each run. It is normally altered between runs in order to investigate the effects of different parameter values.

101

TABLE A.1. SINGLE MINERAL ORE RESERVE FILE

File: RESERV1.DAT

Test reserves single mineral (3 blocks)   High grade block

5	0·1	0·2	1·0
	20	0·0	
	30	0·2	
	40	0·4	
	50	0·6	
	60	0·9	

Test reserves single mineral (3 blocks)   Low grade block

5	0·1	0·2	1·0
	60	0·0	
	50	0·2	
	40	0·4	
	30	0·6	
	20	0·9	

Test reserves single mineral (3 blocks)   Medium grade block

5	0·1	0·2	1·0
	40	0·0	
	40	0·2	
	40	0·4	
	40	0·6	
	40	0·9	

* * * *

Reserves File

A specimen ore reserve file is shown in table A.1. It gives the reserves in three increments. For each increment, the number of grade categories, the minimum grade and the grade interval are quoted on a single line. This line is followed by further lines giving the tonnages and average grades in each category.

Of course, the specimen figures are deliberately simplified. Generally, there will be more categories and more increments. To save manual preparation, a file in a suitable form can be created by a preceding mine planning or scheduling program if one is used for this purpose.

TABLE A.2. SPECIMEN INPUT FILE

File: INPUT.DAT

Single Mineral Demonstration. This demonstration shows the layout of a typical input file with output of two results tables. They are directed to the screen but may be printed too by keying Ctrl. Pr.

TABLES	6	8						
OUTPUT	1							
DISCOUNT	15·0							
STOCKPILES	2							
	0·35	5	0·4					
	0·25	10	0·3					
CONSTANTS								
Y	90							
CAPK	9·5							
CW	·5							

– – – –

TIME	1	2	3	4	5	6	9	10
CAPM	24·0	−1	−1	−1	−1	−1	−1	−1
CAPL	12·0	−1	−1	−1	−1	18·0	−1	−1
F	6·0	−1	−1	−1	7·0	−1	−1	−1
CM	1·25	−1	−1	−1	−1	−1	−1	1·5
CL	3·60	−1	−1	−1	−1	−1	3·1	−1
CK	4·00	−1	−1	−1	−1	−1	−1	−1
FINJ	0·00	−1	−1	−1	15	0	0	0
PRCE	14	15	16	17	18	19	−1	−1

– – – –

TONN	0·0	150	225	300
CAPM	0·0	0·0	6·00	−1
FINJ	0·0		2·0	
CW		·25	0·5	·75

– – – –

Data Input File

A specimen operating data file is shown in table A.2. The operating parameters are named according to mnemonics which are listed in table A.3. The run specified by the data file includes two stockpiles with minimum grades of 0·35 and 0·25, and initial tonnages of 5·0 and 10·0 respectively.

Five parameters are specified as having constant values, eight vary with time, and three have added increments defined by tonnage. This

103

TABLE A.3. INPUT MNEMONIC DEFINITIONS

Single Mineral			*Two Minerals*
CAPM	Mine capacity		CAPM
CAPL	Mill capacity		CAPL
CAPK	Market capacity	— mineral 1	CPK1
		— mineral 2	CPK2
CM	Unit cost mining		CM
CL	Unit cost milling		CL
CK	Unit cost marketing	— mineral 1	CK1
		— mineral 2	CK2
CS ·	Unit cost stockpile pick-up		
Y	Mill recovery (%)	— mineral 1	Y1
		— mineral 2	Y2
PRCE	Price	— mineral 1	PRC1
		— mineral 2	PRC2
F	Period Fixed cost		F
FINJ	Capital injection		FINJ
YS	Mill recovery stockpile material (%)		
CW	Unit cost waste dumping		CW
COG	Cut-off grade	— mineral 1	COG1
	(Calculated if unspecified)	— mineral 2	COG2
QS	Rate of withdrawal from stockpile		

means, in this example, that the mining capacity increases by 6·0 after 225 units of the reserve have been mined and that waste haulage costs increase by 0·25, 0·5 and 0·75 after 150, 225 and 300 units have been mined. A capital injection of 2·0 is made to correspond with the increase in mining capacity.

The treatment plant capacity increases from 12·0 to 18·0 in year 6 and a capital injection of 15·0 occurs the year before. The price increases steadily for the first 6 years, the mining cost increases in year 10, the fixed costs increase in year 5 and the treatment costs decrease in year 9. Two other parameters, the mine capacity and the market costs, are listed as being time dependent, although no particular change is specified. This anomaly can arise during a sequence of runs when changes are sometimes included and sometimes cancelled.

TABLE A.4. PERIOD PRODUCTION TABLE

Optimal Present Value　　　　　*Life*
148·3　　　　　　　　　　27

Period	Major Block	Lim. Capac.	Optimum Cog.	Quantity Mined	Quantity Conc'd	—— Min1 —— Quantity	Grade	Total Cash Flow
1	1	L	0·348	17·08	12·00	7·45	0·690	1·40
2	1	L	0·370	17·64	12·00	7·57	0·701	9·17
3	1	L	0·387	18·10	12·00	7·66	0·709	17·02
4	1	L	0·400	18·47	12·00	7·73	0·715	24·93
5	1	L	0·411	18·77	12·00	7·78	0·721	31·90
6	1	K	0·310	21·24	15·72	9·50	0·671	49·59
7	1	K	0·302	21·13	15·81	9·50	0·667	49·49
8	1	K	0·293	21·04	15·90	9·50	0·664	49·39
9	1	K	0·255	20·71	16·25	9·50	0·650	57·01
10	1	K	0·234	20·57	16·44	9·50	0·642	51·62
11	2	M	0·193	12·26	8·33	4·28	0·571	20·52
12	2	M	0·193	24·00	14·02	6·33	0·502	3·50
13	2	M	0·193	30·00	17·53	7·91	0·502	6·12
14	2	M	0·193	30·00	17·53	7·91	0·502	6·12
15	2	M	0·193	30·00	17·53	7·91	0·502	6·12
16	2	M	0·193	30·00	17·53	7·91	0·502	6·12
17	2	M	0·193	30·00	17·53	7·91	0·502	6·12
18	3	LK	0·242	28·78	17·54	8·49	0·538	17·27
19	3	K	0·244	26·70	17·53	9·50	0·602	36·53
20	3	LK	0·239	26·63	17·60	9·50	0·600	36·49
21	3	LK	0·234	26·55	17·67	9·50	0·597	36·44
22	3	LK	0·229	26·47	17·76	9·50	0·594	36·38
23	3	LK	0·223	26·39	17·85	9·50	0·591	36·31
24	3	LK	0·217	26·30	17·96	9·50	0·588	36·22
25	3	LK	0·219	26·31	17·93	9·50	0·589	36·24
26	4		0·000	4·86	3·35	1·76	0·585	−0·10
27	4		0·000	0·00	0·00	0·00	0·000	−2·65

The −1 symbol causes a repetition of the last specified figure and is necessary to distinguish this requirement from a zero. Unspecified years also automatically cause a repetition of the previous figure. This form of input has been adopted to make the data preparation as simple as possible; generally only changes have to be specified.

The units are inherent in the data and are therefore unstated.

TABLE A.5. STOCKPILE TABLES BY PERIOD

		——— *Stockpile 1* ———				——— *Stockpile 2* ———			
	Major	*Initial*		*Qty.*	*Ave.*	*Initial*		*Qty.*	*Ave.*
Period	*Block*	*Qty.*	*Grade*	*Change*	*Grade*	*Qty.*	*Grade*	*Change*	*Grade*
1	1	5·0	0·40	0·0	0·00	10·0	0·30	1·5	0·27
2	1	5·0	0·40	0·4	0·35	11·5	0·30	1·5	0·27
3	1	5·4	0·39	0·7	0·35	13·0	0·29	1·6	0·27
4	1	6·0	0·39	0·9	0·35	14·5	0·29	1·6	0·27
5	1	7·0	0·38	1·2	0·35	16·2	0·29	1·6	0·27
6	1	8·1	0·37	0·0	0·00	17·8	0·29	1·0	0·25
7	1	8·1	0·37	0·0	0·00	18·9	0·29	0·8	0·25
8	1	8·1	0·37	0·0	0·00	19·7	0·28	0·7	0·25
9	1	8·1	0·37	0·0	0·00	20·4	0·28	0·1	0·25
10	1	8·1	0·37	0·0	0·00	20·5	0·28	0·0	0·00
11	1	8·1	0·37	0·0	0·00	20·5	0·28	0·0	0·00
12	2	8·1	0·37	−8·1	0·37	20·5	0·28	0·0	0·00
13	2	0·0	0·00	0·0	0·00	20·5	0·28	0·0	0·00
14	2	0·0	0·00	0·0	0·00	20·5	0·28	0·0	0·00
15	2	0·0	0·00	0·0	0·00	20·5	0·28	0·0	0·00
16	2	0·0	0·00	0·0	0·00	20·5	0·28	0·0	0·00
17	2	0·0	0·00	0·0	0·00	20·5	0·28	0·0	0·00
18	2	0·0	0·00	0·0	0·00	20·5	0·28	0·0	0·00
19	3	0·0	0·00	0·0	0·00	20·5	0·28	0·0	0·00
20	3	0·0	0·00	0·0	0·00	20·5	0·28	0·0	0·00
21	3	0·0	0·00	0·0	0·00	20·5	0·28	0·0	0·00
22	3	0·0	0·00	0·0	0·00	20·5	0·28	0·0	0·00
23	3	0·0	0·00	0·0	0·00	20·5	0·28	0·0	0·00
24	3	0·0	0·00	0·0	0·00	20·5	0·28	0·0	0·00
25	3	0·0	0·00	0·0	0·00	20·5	0·28	0·0	0·00
26	3	0·0	0·00	0·0	0·00	20·5	0·28	0·0	0·00
27	4	0·0	0·00	0·0	0·00	20·5	0·28	−20·5	0·28

Commonly, they will be millions of tonnes, millions of dollars, dollars per tonne and per cent. Users are free to adopt any units, but they must remain consistent.

Output

The input file requested two of eight possible tables. These are shown here as tables A.4 and A.5. The first table gives production data which indicates that the optimum cut-off policy fluctuates from around 0·4 in the early years to under 0·2 in the middle years and over 0·2 in the later years. The operation is constrained by the treatment plant for the first five years, the market for the next five, the mine for the next seven and finally by a balance between the treatment plant and the market for the last eight years. The life, including two years processing stockpile material at the end, is 27 years. The present value is 148·3.

The second table gives deposits and withdrawals from stock. The higher grade stockpile is depleted as soon as the low-grade ore of increment 2 is encountered, but the lower grade stockpile is left until the reserves are exhausted. Even then it incurs a loss, so the policy of accumulating a lower grade intermediate stockpile would appear unjustified.

Conclusion
This brief description of the OGRE program is intended only to convey an understanding of what it does and how it may be used for mine planning. The rights to the program are owned by RTZ Consultants and more information about it can be obtained from:

> RTZ Consultants Ltd,
> Castlemead,
> Lower Castle Street,
> Bristol BS99 77R,
> U.K.

CASE STUDY 1

Underground Tin

This is an old mine which is nearing the end of its reserves. The deposit is a vein type; the veins generally lie at a shallow angle and average about 3 metres in thickness. Mining is by open stopes and tracked equipment.

Development policy is to maintain sufficient prepared stopes to keep the mill supplied for about a year, but this policy is becoming increasingly difficult to implement as the limits of the mineralised body are approached. As a consequence, the mill operates at 300,000 tonnes per year, although its capacity is 360,000 tonnes per year. The product is a concentrate which is trucked to a local smelter. The net smelter return is 80% of the contained tin value.

Data
Variable costs per unit of ore ($/tonne)

Stoping	7·5	
Tramming ($3 × 1·5 km)	4·5	
Hoisting	5·25	
Milling	12·75	
Total	30·0	(h)
Fixed Costs	$12·15 10^6/year	(f)

Other parameters are:

Recovery	72%	(y)
Forecast tin price	$10,000/tonne	
Net Smelter return	$8,400/tonne	(p)
Marketing costs	$45/tonne	(k)
Development costs	$2·0 10^6/year	

108

TABLE CS 1.1. DEVELOPED RESERVES

			Tonnes (000)	*Estimated recoverable grades (%)*
Level 8	Stope	14	15	0·47
		15	27	1·10
		16	13	1·32
		17	11	1·41
		18	8	0·98
Level 9	Stope	5	24	0·64
		8	7	1·55
		9	14	0·87
		10	13	1·24
		11	5	0·73
Level 10	Stope	4	32	0·40
		5	17	0·83
		6	25	0·69
		10	14	0·92
		11	12	0·59
		12	19	1·18
		13	8	1·04
	Total		264	

Normal Operational Cut-Off Grade

Because the capacity of the operation is limited by the rate of development, the relevant cut-off is the limiting economic cut-off for the mine as described in Chapter 5.

$$g_m = h / (p-k)y$$
$$= 30 / 8,355 \times 0·72$$
$$= 0·50\%$$

Hanging Wall Cut-Off Grade

The footwall is defined by a clear contact but the hanging wall is usually indistinct; the grades gradually decline to barren rock. Thus its precise position is determined by sampling and applying a hanging wall cut-off grade. In these circumstances, it can be assumed that the stope is being mined anyway so that the stoping cost has already been incurred.

Thus, for the hanging wall contact

$$g = (4·5 + 5·25 + 12·75) / 8,355 \times 0·72$$
$$= 0·37\%$$

The currently developed reserves are shown in table CS 1.1

Cash Flow Calculations ($ million)
Applying a cut-off of 0·5% to these reserves, the reserves of ore are 217,000 tonnes at 0·97%. At a throughput of 300,000 tonnes per year, the corresponding cash flow position is (for less than 9 months' operation)

Revenue $0·217 \times 0·97 \times 0·72 \times 83·55$	=	12·66
Variable cost $0·217 \times 30$	=	6·51
Fixed cost $12·15 \times 0·217/0·300$	=	8·79
Development cost $2·0 \times 217/300$	=	1·45
Total cost	=	16·75
Net cash flow (over 9 months)		$-4·09 million

This means that the mine will incur substantial losses if it continues in normal operation. If the decision to close the mine is taken, several situations can occur.

1. Closure in a year's time
The revenue is unaffected because the cut-off remains the same. The development costs are saved but the fixed costs are incurred for the whole year, although the mine runs out of ore in 9 months as before.

Revenue	=	12·66
Variable costs	=	6·51
Fixed costs	=	12·15
Net cash flow (for whole year)		$-6·00 million

2. *Closure when unprofitable*

In this case, the mill should be run at maximum capacity until the ore reserves are exhausted. As the mill will be limiting, the appropriate formula is the limiting economic cut-off for the treatment plant

$$g_h = (h+f/H) / (p-k)y$$
$$= (30 + 12.15/0.36) / 8,355 \times 0.72$$
$$= 1.06\%$$

Applying this cut-off to the reserves gives reserves of ore of 90,000 tons at 1.24%. This is three months' supply, which gives rise to a cash flow of

Revenue $0.09 \times 1.24 \times 0.72 \times 83.55$	=	6.71
Variable cost 0.09×30	=	2.70
Fixed cost $12.15 \times 90/360$	=	3.06
		――――
Net cash flow (over 3 months)		$\$+0.95$ million

3. *Closure in, say, 6 months*

In this case, the cut-off should be chosen to maximise the revenue during the six-month period. This means treating 180,000 tonnes of ore. By inspection, a cut-off of 0.65% gives rise to reserves of ore of 181,000 tonnes at 0.99%. The corresponding cash flow is

Revenue $0.181 \times 0.99 \times 0.72 \times 83.55$	=	10.79
Variable cost 0.181×30	=	5.43
Fixed cost $12.15 \times 181/360$	=	6.07
		――――
Net cash flow (over 6 months)		$\$-0.71$ million

Obviously no decision to close a mine can be taken lightly. In a situation similar to the one described in this study it would depend not only on the profitability of the current developed reserves but also on the prospects for a further development programme. Here, it has been assumed that such prospects are poor so that the development costs are the first to be cut.

CASE STUDY 2

Underground Lead/Zinc

This is a medium-sized underground operation with hoisting and milling capacities of 1·3 million tonnes per year. The mineralised body is wide, steeply dipping and fairly consistent over a strike length of several kilometres, according to pre-production drilling from surface.

The mining method is sublevel caving. The lead content is of secondary importance to the zinc and, as its value is approximately half, lead assays are converted to a zinc equivalent by dividing by two. The reserves are compiled on this basis and grade is controlled wholly by zinc equivalents. Operational grades are determined from channel samples taken along the walls of development cross-cuts. Dilution averages about 15% and metal recoveries from stoping average 88%. The survey tonnages and grades are therefore multiplied by a tonnage factor of 1·15 and a grade factor of 0·77 (0·88/1·15) to yield estimates of the tonnages and grades which will be achieved during the mining process. It is to these figures that cut-offs are applied.

There are two operational cut-offs. One defines the hanging and footwalls beyond which there is no further drilling and blasting. The other defines the point at which material is no longer drawn as ore but is left in the stope as waste. The grades at the draw points are measured regularly by grab samples.

The government took a 51% interest in the mine at the beginning of the year. An intensive financial study at the time valued the property on the basis of its cash earning potential at $150 million, using a discount rate before tax of 15%.

Data
Variable unit costs ($/tonne ore)

Drilling and Blasting	3·6
Mucking	1·5
Haulage	3·2
Hoisting	6·8
Milling	11·4

Total	26·5	(h)

Fixed costs	$15·3 million/year	(f)
Mill capacity	1·3 million tonnes/year	(H)
Mill recovery	81%	(y)
Forecast Zn price	(i) $750/tonne Zn in concentrate	(p)
(net smelter)		
	(ii) $650/tonne Zn year 1	
	$750/tonne Zn thereafter	
Shipping and insurance	$35/tonne Zn	(k)

Cut-Off Calculations
Because the hoisting and milling capacity is limiting throughput, the relevant cut-off grade formula is the limiting economic cut-off for the treatment plant which is derived in Chapter 5.

$$g_h = \{h + (f+F) / H\} / (p-k)y$$

Assuming constant economic conditions in the future, F is given by

$$F = \delta V$$
$$= \$0·15 \times 150 \text{ million}$$
$$= \$22·5 \text{ million}$$

h takes two different values depending upon the cut-off under consideration.

1. Hanging and Footwall Cut-Off

In this case all the variable costs are incurred if material is classified as ore instead of wall rock.

$$h = \$26{\cdot}5/\text{tonne}$$

and $g = \{26{\cdot}5 + (15{\cdot}3 + 22{\cdot}5)/1{\cdot}3\} \, / \, \{(750 - 35) \times 0{\cdot}81\}$

$$= 55{\cdot}6 \, / \, 579$$
$$= 9{\cdot}6\%$$

2. Draw Point Cut-Off

At this point the drilling and blasting costs have already been incurred. Therefore, only the remainder are affected so

$$h = \$22{\cdot}9/\text{tonne}$$

and $g = 52{\cdot}0 \, / \, 579$

$$= 9{\cdot}0\%$$

These figures are high because of the inclusion of $22·5 million for F. If the mine were nearing the end of its life, as in Case Study 1, or if it were teetering on the brink of profitability, the draw cut-off grade would be given by

$$g = \{22{\cdot}9 + 15{\cdot}3/1{\cdot}3\} \, / \, (750 - 35) \times 0{\cdot}81$$
$$= 34{\cdot}7 \, / \, 579$$
$$= 6{\cdot}0\%$$

Further, if the mill were at any time to be starved of feed, the cut-off could be reduced to the mine cut-off to make good the deficiency. This, for the draw cut-off, is given by

$$g = 22{\cdot}9 \, / \, 579$$
$$= 4{\cdot}0\%$$

Price Change Effect

The effect of a price change may be illustrated by assuming that there is a sudden drop in price from the estimated figure of $750 per tonne net of smelter charges to $650 per tonne. Assuming an average head grade of, say, 14% this will cause a corresponding drop in revenue of about $14·7 million per year. If this is judged to be only a temporary

114

phenomenon, with the price recovering to its forecast level within a year, then

Present value now
$$= 150 - 14{\cdot}7 / (1{\cdot}0 + 0{\cdot}15)$$
$$= \$137{\cdot}2 \text{ million}$$

Present value a year hence but with the same reserves as now
$$= \$150 \text{ million}$$

(The price is assumed to recover to the level at which the present value of $150 million was originally estimated).

Therefore

dV/dT = (Present value a year hence) − (Present value now)
$$= \$12{\cdot}8 \text{ million}$$

and $F = \delta V - dV/dT$
$$= 0{\cdot}15 \times 137{\cdot}2 - 12{\cdot}8$$
$$= \$7{\cdot}8 \text{ million}$$

Substituting this value in the draw cut-off formula

$g = \{22{\cdot}9 + (15{\cdot}3 + 7{\cdot}8)/1{\cdot}3\} / (650 - 35) \times 0{\cdot}81$
$$= 40{\cdot}7 / 498$$
$$= 8{\cdot}2\%$$

Thus the formula indicates that in response to a temporary price drop, the cut-off grade should be slightly lowered from 9% to 8·2%. This result is in stark contrast to all other cut-off formulae which indicate an increase because of the smaller denominator.

Open Pit — Uranium

This is a medium-sized open pit operation which was brought into production on the back of firm government contracts for the product. These contracts have a further five years to run. Beyond this, the future is uncertain, although the directors are optimistic despite the lack of any present spot demand. Because the development was financed with the help of soft loans, a discount rate of 10% before tax is used for the cost of capital. Current operational cash flow is about $15 million per year. Over five years at 10% this yields a present value of $57 million.

By that time, the reserves will be only 25% depleted and the directors consider that the remainder should be assigned at least the same value. They have, therefore, assessed a valuation of $60 million for the operation beyond the end of the fifth year.

The contracts are for 900 tonnes per year. The price is undisclosed but, for the purpose of this exercise, a figure of $60 per kg ex-mine is used. The mine was specifically designed to meet the contract requirements. The pit equipment can move about 12 million tonnes per year from the pit and the concentrator capacity is just short of 4 million tonnes per year.

Data
Capacities
Mining	12 million tonnes/year	(M)
Treating	3·9 million tonnes/year	(H)
Marketing	900 tonnes/year	(K)

116

Variable unit costs

Mining	$1·32/tonne of material	(m)
Treating	$3·41/tonne ore	(h)

Property taxes	$1·78/year ⎫	
Overheads	$3·82/year ⎬	(f)
Other fixed	$6·30/year ⎭	

Price	$60/kilo	(p)
Recovery	87%	(100y)
Cost of capital	10% before tax	(100δ)
Present value now	${57 + 60/(1·1)^5}$ million = $94·3 million	(V*)
Present value next year	${47·5 + 60/(1·1)^4}$ million = $88·5 million	
Change in P.V.	−$5·8 million	(dV*/dT)
Opportunity cost	${0·1 × 94·3 + 5·8}$ million = $15·2 million	(δV* − dV*/dT) (F)

Limiting Economic Cut-Off Grades
Applying the formulae from Chapter 5

$$g_m = h / (p-k)y$$
$$= 3·41 / 60 × 0·87$$
$$= 0·07 \text{ kg/tonne}$$

$$g_h = \{h + (f+\delta V/H)\} / (p-k)y$$
$$= [3·41 + \{11·90 + (0·01 × 94·3)\}/3·9] / 60 × 0·87$$
$$= 0·17 \text{ kg/tonne}$$

$$g_k = h / \{p - (f+\delta V)/K\}y$$
$$= 3·41 / \{60 - (11·9 + 9·43) / 0·9\} × 0·87$$
$$= 0·11 \text{ kg/tonne}$$

Balancing Cut-Off Grades
As there is no prior reason for any one of these to be the effective optimum cut-off grade, the actual grades available for mining in the immediate future must be analysed. Table CS3.1 gives typical figures

117

TABLE CS3.1.
MINE PLAN FOR THE NEXT 3 MILLION TONNES FROM THE PIT

Uranium categories (kg/tonne)	Tonnes (k)	Grade (kg/t)	Mineral (kgs)	A Cumulative tonnes	B Cumulative mineral	Ratio A/2975	Ratio B/2975	Ratio B/A
	1,540			2,975		1·0		
0·1								
	82	·112	9·184	1,435	334·319	0·468	·112	0·23
0·12								
	143	·129	18·447	1,353	325·135	0·45	·109	0·24
0·14								
	129	·153	19·737	1,210	306·688	0·41	·103	0·25
0·16								
	152	·172	26·144	1,081	286·951	0·36	·096	0·27
0·18								
	134	·188	25·192	929	260·807	0·31	·088	0·28
0·20								
	117	·207	24·219	795	235·615	0·27	·079	0·29
0·22								
	93	·230	21·930	678	211·396	0·23	·071	0·31
0·24								
	59	·254	14·986	585	189·466	0·20	·064	0·32
0·26								
	78	·271	21·138	526	174·48	0·18	·059	0·33
0·28								
	63	·289	18·207	448	153·342	0·15	·052	0·34
0·30								
	385	·351	135·135	385	135·135	0·13	·045	0·35
Total	2,975							

for a short-term mine plan covering about three months' production or the next 3 million tonnes from the pit. As described in Chapter 6, such a plan implies that the three components of the mining system will balance in pairs at certain cut-off grades. These can be calculated by extending the table of tonnages and grades to include mineral contents and cumulative totals above each grade level as shown in table CS3.1. Then the ratios of potential ore to total material, corresponding mineral to total material, and mineral to potential ore can be calculated also. The balancing cut-off grades are where these ratios equate to the corresponding capacity ratios.

Allowing for recovery, the capacities are

$$M = 12 \qquad H = 3·9 \qquad K = 1·034 \ (0·9/0·87)$$

Hence the ratios are

$$H/M = 0·33 \qquad K/M = 0·086 \qquad K/H = 0·27$$

118

By inspection from the table:

$g_{mh} = 0.17$ kg/tonne
$g_{mk} = 0.18$ kg/tonne
$g_{hk} = 0.16$ kg/tonne

Effective Optimum Cut-Off Grade
Now, referring to the formulae in Chapter 7

$G_{mh} = 0.17$ $(g_m = 0.07, g_{mh} = 0.17, g_h = 0.17)$
$G_{mk} = 0.11$ $(g_m = 0.07, g_k = 0.11, g_{mk} = 0.18)$
$G_{hk} = 0.16$ $(g_k = 0.11, g_{hk} = 0.16, g_h = 0.17)$

Therefore the effective optimum cut-off grade is the middle of the three, namely 0.16 kg per tonne. This is the cut-off at which the concentrator and the market are just in balance, both at full capacity.

Cash Flow Calculation
Although the tonnage in the mine plan is sufficient for only a part year, a yearly equivalent cash flow can be estimated ($ million)

Revenue 900 × 1,000 × 60	= 54	
Mining cost (3.9/0.36) × 1.32	= 14.3	
Concentrating cost 3.9 × 3.41	= 13.3	
Fixed costs	= 11.9	
Total costs	= 39.5	
Net cash flow	$14.5 million per year	

This figure compares satisfactorily with the initial figure of $15.0 million on which the present value estimate was based. Had the discrepancy been large, a new present value could be estimated and the calculation repeated. More than one iteration is seldom necessary to achieve satisfactory consistency.

Sensitivity to Present Value Estimate
The present value estimate in this case is not well founded, so it is instructive to examine the extent to which the cut-off is affected by different present value assumptions. Taking a range of plus and

minus 50% in the residual present value estimate of $60 million:

$$V1 = 57 + 90 / (1 \cdot 1)^5 = \$113 \cdot 0 \text{ million}$$
$$V2 = 57 + 30 / (1 \cdot 1)^5 = \$ 75 \cdot 6 \text{ million}$$

Substituting these figures and repeating the cut-off calculations:

	V1	V2
$g_m =$	$0 \cdot 07$	$0 \cdot 07$ kg/tonne
$g_h =$	$0 \cdot 18$	$0 \cdot 16$ kg/tonne
$g_k =$	$0 \cdot 11$	$0 \cdot 10$ kg/tonne

The balancing cut-offs are unaltered so:

$G_{mh} =$	$0 \cdot 17$	$0 \cdot 16$ kg/tonne
$G_{mk} =$	$0 \cdot 21$	$0 \cdot 10$ kg/tonne
$G_{hk} =$	$0 \cdot 16$	$0 \cdot 16$ kg/tonne

The effective optimum cut-off grade therefore remains the same at $0 \cdot 16$ kg per tonne. This is an example of an operation that is closely confined by the three component capacities and relatively insensitive to economic variations.

Open Pit Copper/Molybdenum

This mine was opened only recently. It is based upon a mineralised body of limited extent lying just below the surface. A drilling programme indicated a mineralised tonnage of about 12 million, and a preliminary open pit study showed that most of this tonnage could be recovered from an ultimate pit which, including overburden, contained 15 million tonnes of total material.

An analysis of the tonnage in both copper and molybdenum categories was derived from a polygonal representation of the reserves based upon borehole data. The results of this analysis are summarised in table CS4.1.

A treatment plant of 750,000 tonnes per year capacity was proposed and the total capital cost for the plant, access roads, water, power, sewerage, offices and engineering was estimated at less than $8 million. The money was raised locally and the operation was brought on stream early and within budget. The investors expect a return of at least 20% on their money. Mining is undertaken by a local civil engineering contractor. Detailed long-term mine plans are considered unnecessary, but a rough plan for the next million tonnes or so of excavation is maintained in order to direct the contractor's activities.

For practical convenience, the grades for this plan are based solely on copper, and grade is controlled in the pit wholly by copper assays from blasthole dust samples. The present cut-off is 0·3% Cu. When necessary for value estimates, the molybdenum is converted to a copper equivalent at a ratio of 1:4. This is thought to represent the price and recovery differentials and the relatively volatile nature of

TABLE CS4.1. SPECIMEN TWO MINERAL RESERVE — COPPER/MOLYBDENUM

Copper Categories (%)	Molybdenum Categories (%)					Total	Cu/Equivalent⊘
	Less than ·025	·026-·050	·051-·075	·076-·100	Over ·100		
Less than 0·10	1,320	900	285	315	510	3,330	·330
0·11-0·20	360† ·12* ·017**	300 ·17 ·031	240 ·16 ·06	135 ·19 ·085	60 ·14 ·114	1,095 ·152 ·044	·398
0·21-0·30	735 ·25 ·011	525 ·27 ·028	300 ·25 ·066	210 ·22 ·091	30 ·26 ·127	1,800 ·252 ·036	·472
0·31-0·40	1,110 ·33 ·031	570 ·32 ·042	375 ·35 ·058	135 ·34 ·094	30 ·37 ·138	2,220 ·332 ·035	·559
0·41-0·50	525 ·44 ·006	255 ·47 ·035	75 ·45 ·054	60 ·48 ·091	30 ·46 ·119	945 ·452 ·027	·725
0·51-0·60	510 ·53 ·012	300 ·55 ·039	210 ·57 ·070	105 ·54 ·082	90 ·55 ·152	1,215 ·544 ·045	·824
0·61-0·70	375 ·67 ·014	270 ·63 ·029	210 ·65 ·062	90 ·64 ·085	90 ·66 ·120	1,035 ·652 ·043	1·254
Greater than 0·70	645 ·98 ·009	690 1·04 ·038	570 1·02 ·063	495 1·09 ·086	360 1·01 ·128	2,760 1·027 ·057	
Total	5,580	3,810	2,265	1,545	1,200	14,400	

† Tonnes (000); * Average Copper %; ** Average Molybdenum %: this pattern followed throughout table.
⊘ Molybdenum/Copper Value Equivalence = 4/1

the molybdenum market. So far, production has been reasonably consistent with the reserve estimates.

Data

Treatment plant capacity	750,000 tonnes	(H)
Mining cost	$1·06/tonne mined	(m)
Treatment cost	$3·52/tonne ore	(h)
Marketing cost	$63/tonne Cu	(k)
Fixed costs	$790,000/year	(f)
Recovery	82%	(y)
Forecast price	$1,700/tonne Cu	
Royalty	1·5%	
Price net of Royalty	$1,674·5/tonne Cu	(p)

Present Value Estimate at 0·3% Cu Cut-Off
From the reserve estimates, at 0·3% Cu:

Ore:material	= 8,175:14,400	= 0·57
Average grade	= 0·83% Copper equivalent	

Therefore the annual cash flow is given by ($ million):

Revenue $0·75 \times 0·83 \times 0·82 \times (1,674·5-63) / 100$
$$= 8·22$$

Costs

Mining ($0·75 \times 1·06/0·57$)	= 1·40
Treatment ($0·75 \times 3·52$)	= 2·64
Fixed costs	= 0·79
	——
Total costs	= 4·96
	——
Net cash flow	= $3·39
Mine life	11·4 years
Present value at 20%	= $14·8 million

Cut-Off Calculation

This estimated present value can be used to calculate a new cut-off grade. The relevant formula from Chapter 5 is the limiting economic grade for the treatment component.

$$g_h = \{h + (f+F)/H\} / (p-k)y$$
$$= \{3 \cdot 52 + (0 \cdot 79 + 2 \cdot 97)/0 \cdot 75\} / (1,700-63) \times \cdot 985 \times \cdot 82$$
$$= 0 \cdot 65\%$$

However, this is a case of a parametric measure because the copper categories are inconsistent with the average copper equivalents within each category. The calculated cut-off of 0·65% applies to the copper equivalent. Interpolating by inspection from table CS4.1, a 0·65% average copper equivalent grade corresponds to about 0·51% original copper grade. For convenience, take a figure of 0·50%.

Present Value Estimate at 0·5% Cut-Off

Again from the reserve estimates at 0·5% cut-off

Ore:material	= 5,010:14,400	= 0·35
Average grade	= 1·037% Copper equivalent	

Therefore the annual cash flow is given by ($ million):

Revenue $\{0 \cdot 75 \times 1 \cdot 037 \times 0 \cdot 82 \times (1,674 \cdot 5 - 63) / 100\}$
$= 10 \cdot 28$

Costs
- Mining $(0 \cdot 75 \times 1 \cdot 06/0 \cdot 35)$ = 2·29
- Treatment $(3 \cdot 52 \times 0 \cdot 75)$ = 2·64
- Fixed costs = 0·79

Total cost = 5·72

Net cash flow = 4·56
Mine life 6·96 years
Present value at 20% = $16·1 million

124

Final Cut-Off Determination

This present value estimate of $16·1 million could be substituted in the formula for the cut-off grade and the whole calculation repeated, but the change would only be small. A cut-off at 0·50% Cu is therefore as good an estimate as can be achieved by this technique.

In fact, the optimum cut-off policy must achieve a higher present value than $16·1 million. It involves a cut-off declining from 0·50% in the first year to about 0·26% in the seventh year as the present value declines.

A fixed cut-off of 0·50% is therefore sub-optimum. However, the discrepancy between the present value estimated in this way and the actual optimum present value is rarely of any significance when the sole purpose of the calculation is the determination of a current cut-off value. The approximation is small compared with the assumptions implicit in the reserve estimates and the economic uncertainties in the future.

Calculating a Complete Cut-Off Policy

As the reserve estimates have been made for the whole mineralised body, it is possible in this case to calculate a complete cut-off policy for the life of the mine. Assuming the same data with constant economic conditions, the results are shown in table CS4.2. They have been obtained using the OGRE program.

TABLE CS4.2

Year	Cut-Off Grade (% Cu)	Tonnes (000) Mined	Tonnes (000) Treated	Net Cash Flow ($M)
1	0·50	2,160	750	4·56
2	0·50	2,160	750	4·56
3	0·49	2,130	750	4·54
4	0·48	2,070	750	4·49
5	0·46	2,020	750	4·43
6	0·38	1,680	750	3·95
7	0·30	1,320	750	3·38
8	0·26	870	540	2·25

Present value $16·4 million

This confirms the adequacy of the previous determination.

125

Evaluating Expansion Schemes

Output is limited by the treatment plant so expansion proposals are only concerned with extensions to this plant. Engineering considerations indicate a natural increment in capacity of 0·5 million tonnes per year. The associated capital cost including extensions to supporting facilities where necessary is estimated at $4·0 million. Procurement and construction time is estimated at a year.

Treating Marginal Material

One expansion strategy to consider is the use of extended treatment plant capacity to process material which is currently being dumped but which is above the mine cut-off grade and would, therefore, be processed if there were sufficient capacity to do so. This is often called marginal material.

For an extended plant the mine cut-off grade is below 0·2% Cu. Using a cut-off of 0·5% Cu for the first year and 0·2% Cu thereafter gives the same mine life, 7·7 years, as the optimum policy before expansion, and the corresponding present value is $19·5 million.

This is an increase of $3·1 million on the optimum at 750,000 tonnes per year capacity but at a capital cost of $4·0 million is not a justifiable investment.

TABLE CS4.3

Year	Cut-Off Grade (% Cu)	Tonnes (000) Mined	Tonnes (000) Treated	Net Cash Flow ($M)
1	0·48	2,070	750	4·49
2	0·47	3,410	1,250	7·96
3	0·42	3,080	1,250	7·52
4	0·31	2,290	1,250	6·32
5	0·29	2,130	1,250	6·01
6	0·17	1,410	1,000	4·14

Present value $20·5 million

This is an increase of $4·1 million on the optimum for the present plant and therefore promises an adequate return.

126

Optimum Cut-Off Policy
With the same assumptions about plant capacities, namely 750,000 tonnes per year for the first year and 1,250,000 tonnes per year thereafter, the optimum cut-off policy can be calculated. This is shown in table CS4.3.

CASE STUDY 5

Underground Gold

This is a deep mine typical of the reef mines in South Africa. It has been in operation for over 25 years. Most of the claim area has been developed and there are few remaining places where the grades are untested. Fully developed reserves for which detailed grade tonnage compilations have been made amount to almost 7 million tonnes. A further 8 million tonnes is judged to conform to approximately the same distribution. Therefore, for this study a single grade tonnage table for the whole 15 million tonnes has been assumed to be applicable.

Beyond this, a residual value of $50 million has been attached to the remaining reserves which consist of several areas that were not fully exploited because they were judged insufficiently promising while the main reef areas were still being developed.

From the mass of statistics accumulated over the years, a relationship between the predicted grades and the actual grades has been established. It is based upon comparisons between the sample results taken during development and panel sample results taken subsequently during mining. The relationship indicates that the lower grades are underestimated and the higher grades overestimated. It is approximately linear. The effect could be integrated into the grade tonnage data by adjusting the grade estimate for each stope. However, it is administratively tidier to keep the adjustments separate. Here the relationship is summarised by a simple table of the average comparisons.

Detailed costings are available but the allocation of certain costs needs close attention, particularly in relation to capital costs, working costs and development costs. Strictly, according to the economic concepts underlying the definition of ore, a capital cost is an expenditure related to establishing or increasing the capacity of a component of the mining system. Other capital costs are either related to replacement and maintenance or to opening up more of the reef.

A capital investment for the purpose of expanding capacity affects the calculation of the present value stream — the capital injection immediately increases the subsequent present values — but it has no direct effect on the calculation of the optimum cut-off grades. It does not appear in the formula for the limiting economic cut-off except through the agency of the present value term itself.

Similarly, capital expenditure for opening up the reef affects the cash flow, and hence the present value stream, but it has no direct effect on the calculation of the optimum cut-off grade. It is essentially part of the term m, and is a cost which is incurred to gain access to potential ore regardless of whether or not the material is eventually classified as ore. On the other hand, all replacement and maintenance expenditure which is judged as necessary for the continuation of the operation at current levels is effectively a fixed or time cost. As such, whether it is capital expenditure or not, it can be counted as part of the term f.

The case study analysis compares the cut-off grade derived from a straight breakeven calculation with those obtained by maximising the present value gross of tax and net of tax.

Data

Capacity	1·75 million tonne/year	(H)

Variable Costs per unit of ore ($/tonne)

Stoping	13·5	
Transport	3·3	
Hoisting	3·9	
Processing	6·4	
Total	27·1	(h)

Fixed Costs ($ million/year)
Pumping and
    Ventilation   2·8
    Amenities   5·1
    Services   9·9
    Administration   3·6
    Sundries   3·9

                25·3

Replacement and
    Maintenance capital   19·4

Total Fixed	44·7	(f)
Development Costs	$4·3/tonne mineralised material	(m)
Recovery	96%	(y)
Net Gold price	$15/g	(p−k)
Tax	Y% = 60 − 360/X	
Where	X = profit net of capital as percentage of revenue	
Cost of capital	7% net of tax	(δ')
	14% gross of tax	(δ)

Residual Present Value $50 million

1) Breakeven Cut-Off Grade
A breakeven cut-off is normally based on the total costs of the operation including overheads and maintenance capital. Development costs are normally excluded as sunk costs but, of course, they do affect the cash flow. The costs are reasonably well defined in this case with the possible exception of development costs. The quoted figure of $4·3 per tonne is the average cost of development of each tonne added to the reserve. It has already been incurred for the 7 million tonnes of material classified as developed; it has yet to be incurred for

TABLE CS5.1

GRADE TONNAGE TABLE (ESTIMATED STOPE VALUES)			RELATIONSHIP — PREDICTED v. ACTUAL GRADES (g/tonne)	
Grade (g/tonne)	Cumulative Tonnes (millions)	Average Grade (g/tonne)	Predicted Grades	Corresponding Average Actual Grades
0·0	15·0	—		
3·0	12·7	5·53	3·0	3·5
3·5	10·8	5·93	4·0	4·2
4·0	9·0	6·36	5·0	4·8
4·5	7·4	6·82	6·0	5·4
5·0	6·0	7·30	7·0	6·0

the remainder of the claim area. It is assumed in the following analysis that the development policy is to maintain about 7 million tonnes of developed reserves. Therefore, the annual rate of development is adjusted according to the cut-off grade so that the newly developed reserves yield 1·75 million tonnes of payable ore.

The straight breakeven formula is:

$$g = \{h + f/H\} \ / \ (p-k)y$$
$$g = \{27·1 + 44·7/1·75\} \ / \ 0·96 \times 15$$
$$= 52·6/14·4$$
$$= 3·7 \ g/tonne$$

Referring to the table of Predicted v. Actual Grades (CS5.1), an actual cut-off of 3·7 g per tonne corresponds to a cut-off of about 3·3 g per tonne applied to predicted grades. At this cut-off, the reserve table shows 11·6 million tonnes of ore at an average predicted grade of 5·77 g per tonne. Again, referring to the Predicted v. Actual Grade table, an average predicted grade of 5·77 g per tonne corresponds to an average actual grade of 5·26 g per tonne. (This direct conversion of average values is only valid for a linear relationship.) Summarising, a breakeven calculation gives:

Cut-off grade   3·3 g/tonne
Tonnage of ore   11·6 million tonnes
Average grade   5·26 g/tonne

The corresponding cash flow before tax, taking the development costs per tonne of ore as $\$4\cdot3 \times 15/11\cdot6 = 5\cdot56$, is

$$C = (14\cdot4 \times 5\cdot26 - 52\cdot6 - 5\cdot56) \times 1\cdot75$$
$$= \$30\cdot8 \text{ million}$$

As a percentage of revenue:

$X = 30\cdot8/132\cdot6$	$= 23\cdot2\%$
$Y = 60 - 360/23\cdot2$	$= 44\cdot5\%$
$\text{Tax} = 30\cdot8 \times 0\cdot445$	$= \$13\cdot7\,\text{million}$

Hence the cash flow net of tax is:

$$C' = \$17\cdot1 \text{ million}$$

The life of the remaining reserves is:

$$11\cdot6/1\cdot75 = 6\cdot63 \text{ years}$$

The present values are, approximately:

Before Tax   PV $= 30\cdot8 \times 4\cdot14 + 0\cdot41 \times 50 = \$148$ million
After Tax   PV $= 17\cdot1 \times 5\cdot16 + 0\cdot64 \times 50 = \$120$ million

Optimum cut-off grade policies will give rise to higher present values so these figures can be rounded up to arrive at suitable initial estimates for the optimum formulae.

2) Before Tax Optimum
Assuming a present value of $\$155$ million and applying the formula for the economic cut-off with the treatment plant limiting:

$$g = \{h + (f+F)/H\}/(p-k)y$$
$$= \{27\cdot1 + (44\cdot7+0\cdot14\times155)/1\cdot75\}/15 \times 0\cdot96$$
$$= \{27\cdot1 + 37\cdot9\}/14\cdot4$$
$$= 4\cdot5 \text{ g/tonne}$$

The corresponding predicted grade is also $4\cdot5$ g per tonne and the tonnage is $7\cdot4$ million at an average predicted grade of $6\cdot82$ g per tonne. This corresponds to an average actual grade of 5·89 g per tonne. Thus

Cut-off grade   4·5 g/tonne
Tonnage of ore   7·4 million
Average grade 5·89 g/tonne

The cash flow before tax (development costs 4·3 × 15/7·4) is

$$C = (14·4 \times 5·89 - 52·6 - 8·7) \times 1·75$$
$$= \$41·1 \text{ million}$$

As a percentage of revenue:

X = 41·1/148·4	= 27·7%
Y = 60 − 360/27·7	= 47%
Tax = 41·1 × 0·47	= $19·3 million

Hence the cash flow net of tax

$$C' = \$21·8 \text{ million}$$

3) After Tax Optimum
Assuming a net of tax present value of $125 million and applying the formula quoted in Chapter 17:

$$g = \{0·4h + (0·4f+F')/H\}/0·436(p-k)y$$
$$= \{0·4 \times 27·1 + (17·9+8·8)/1·75\}/0·436 \times 14·4$$
$$= 4·2 \text{ g/tonne}$$

An actual cut-off of 4·2 g per tonne corresponds to a predicted grade cut-off of 4·0 g per tonne with a tonnage of 9·0 million, an average predicted grade of 6·36 g per tonne and an average actual grade of 5·62 g per tonne. Thus

Cut-off grade	4·0 g/tonne
Tonnage of ore	9·0 million tonnes
Average grade	5·62 g/tonne

The corresponding cash flow before tax (development costs 4·3 × 15/9) is:

$$C = (14{\cdot}4 \times 5{\cdot}62 - 52{\cdot}6 - 7{\cdot}2) \times 1{\cdot}75$$
$$= \$37{\cdot}0 \text{ million}$$

As a percentage of revenue:

$X = 37{\cdot}0/141{\cdot}6$	$= 26{\cdot}1\%$
$Y = 60 - 360/26{\cdot}1$	$= 46{\cdot}2\%$
$\text{Tax} = 37{\cdot}0 \times 0{\cdot}462$	$= \$17{\cdot}1 \text{ million}$

Hence the cash flow net of tax is

$$C' = \$19{\cdot}9 \text{ million}$$

Summary

		Break Even	Optimum Before Tax (year 1)	Optimum After Tax (year 1)
Predicted Grade Cut-off	(g/tonne)	3·3	4·5	4·0
Actual Grade Cut-off	(g/tonne)	3·7	4·5	4·2
Average Predicted Grade	(g/tonne)	5·77	6·82	6·36
Average Actual Grade	(g/tonne)	5·26	5·89	5·62
Tonnage of Ore	(10^6)	11·6	7·4	9·0
Revenue	$(\$10^6)$	133	148	142
Gross Cash Flow	$(\$10^6)$	30·8	41·1	37·0
Net Cash Flow	$(\$10^6)$	17·1	21·8	19·9
Life of Reserves	(years)	6·63	5·83	6·02
Before Tax PV	$(\$10^6)$	148	155	153
After Tax PV	$(\$10^6)$	120	120	120

The present values for the two cases corresponding to the optimum cut-off policies are not simple to calculate because they entail changing cut-offs from year to year. They have been calculated using the OGRE program.

It is apparent that in this case the present value after tax is comparatively insensitive to the cut-off grade policy. The result is a consequence of the particular assumptions and is not one which can be generalised.

Open Pit Copper Pre-feasibility Study

This is a large low grade porphyry copper prospect for which a mining company holds a five year exploration licence. The licence is due to expire in six months time so the company has to decide on its future programme. For this reason it has commissioned a pre-feasibility study into the likely economics of an operation based upon the deposit as it is currently outlined.

About 50 holes have been drilled so far to depths varying from 200 metres to 500 metres. The samples indicate a vertical plug structure within which four geological zones have been identified. A central higher grade core is surrounded by two lower grade irregular tubes and the whole is embedded in an extensive low grade enveloping matrix. Most of the 50 holes are inclined so there is some information about the way grades vary both horizontally and vertically. Variograms have been compiled for each zone and used to estimate grade/tonnage curves based upon a minimum mining block size of about $10 \times 10 \times 10$ metres (1000 cubic metres).

A first trial pit has been designed; this works from a base in the central core and expands upwards at 45° — the initial estimate of the safe slope angle. The trial pit contains about 600 million tonnes of material. Within this ultimate limit five intermediate shells have been positioned to represent intermediate development. They define six pit increments for which grade tonnage tables have been constructed by combining the curves for the zones in the proportions in which they occur in each increment. This is a very approximate procedure but it yields a satisfactory basis for preliminary cut-off analyses and economic evaluations.

Data

Capacities

Mining	24 million tonnes/year (increased to 30 million tonnes/year after year 18)	(M)
Milling (Treating)	12 million tonnes/year (increased to 18 million tonnes/year after year 9)	(H)
Smelting (Marketing)	110,000 tonnes/year	(K)

Capital Costs

For Mine expansion	$2 million
For Mill expansion	$15 million

Variable units costs

Mining	$1·25/tonne of material	(m)
Milling	$3·60/tonne of ore (decreasing to $3·10/tonne after year 9)	(h)
Smelting	$400/tonne of Cu	(k)
Stockpile Reclaim	$0·20/tonne of material	(s)
Fixed Costs	$6·0 million/year (increasing to $7·0 million after year 9)	(f)
Recovery	90%	
Price	$1,400 rising $1,900/tonne Cu by year 6	(p)
Stockpile	Reject material above 0·25% Cu	

Initial capacity parameters are 12 million tonnes per year for the mill and double this for the pit equipment. The plan is to treat the concentrate on site and a smelter of 110,000 tonnes per year capacity has been included in the capital estimates.

The OGRE program has been applied for evaluation purposes and early runs revealed that the proposed mine and mill capacities were inadequate to keep the smelter supplied during the later phases of the pit when the grades declined. Therefore the mill capacity has been increased by 50% after the second pit increment (about 9 years) and the mine by 25% after the fourth increment (about 18 years).

The present copper price is considered low but economists' estimates are that it will remain low for several years and then slowly improve. The earliest date at which a mine could be opened on this prospect is at least five years hence so the price is conservatively assumed to improve slowly thereafter.

Stockpiling is considered an important issue because dumping grades which could conceivably be treated is politically unacceptable. The critical grade is generally thought to be 0·25%Cu.

Basic Evaluation
The Base Case is run without escalation because it is company policy to assume that inflation will affect prices and costs to a corresponding degree. The projected production and cash flow statistics are shown in tables CS6.1 and CS6.2. Only one set of figures is quoted for each increment because they vary little between the years.

During the first four years, the cut-off is determined by the balance between the mill and the smelter with the mine slightly under capacity. During the next four years the position is much the same but the mill is limiting and both the mine and the smelter are operating at just below capacity. For the next nine years, because the mill capacity is much higher, the mine is limiting; the cut-off is low in order to maximise the tonnage going to the mill. Even so the copper production drops well below the smelter capacity during increment 4. It would drop further still in increments 5 and 6 but for the increase in the mine capacity which compensates to some extent. Nonetheless the smelter remains under utilised.

The capacities are actually well matched for the first 12 years of production. The later years could be improved with further expansions to the mine and the mill but the effect on the economics would not be large because the changes are so far in the future.

137

Table CS6.1 Pit Production: Annual Figures

Increment	Period (years)	Limiting Capacity	Optimum Cut-off (%)	Tonnage Mined (M)	Tonnage Waste (M)	Tonnage to Stock (M)	Tonnage to Mill (M)
1	1-4	Mill/Market	0·53	22·2	5·2	5·0	12·0
2	5-8	Mill	0·52	23·5	6·0	5·5	12·0
3	9-12	Mine	0·23	24·0	6·4	—	17·6
4	13-17	Mine	0·23	24·0	7·2	—	16·8
5	18-21	Mine/Mill	0·27	30·0	11·1	0·9	18·0
6	22-26	Mine/Mill	0·30*	22*	11·2*	—	10·8*

Size of Stockpile   50 million tonnes, grade 0·34%Cu

*Typical figures for the period

Table CS6.2 Copper Production: Annual Figures

Increment	Period (years)	Tonnage Milled (M)	Tonnage ex pit (M)	Tonnage ex stock (M)	Average Grade (%)	Average Grade	Copper (000 tonnes)	Cash Flow ($million)
1	1-4	12·0	12·0	—	1·02	—	109	33-71†
2	5-8	12·0	12·0	—	0·95	—	102	74·8
3	9-12	17·6	17·6	—	0·69	—	109	71·4
4	13-17	16·8	16·8	—	0·62	—	93	51·0
5	18-21	18·0	18·0	—	0·58	—	94	40·9
6	22-26	18·0	10·8*	7·2*	0·53*	0·34*	74*	18·8*

Present Value $365 million

*Typical figures for the period

†Increasing cash flow because of increasing prices

Table CS6.3
Increment 6 with Stockpiles (Mine/Mill Limiting)

Year	Cut-off Grade (%)	Tonnage Milled (M)	Tonnage ex pit (M)	Average Grade (%)	Tonnage ex stock (M)	Average Grade (%)	Copper (000 tonnes)	Cash Flow ($million)
21	0·33	17·7	14·9	0·58	2·8	0·34	86	32·0
22	0·31	18·0	10·8	0·54	7·2	0·34	74	18·9
23	0·30	18·0	10·8	0·53	7·2	0·34	74	18·8
24	0·29	18·0	10·8	0·53	7·2	0·34	73	18·7
25	0·28	18·0	12·6	0·52	5·4	0·34	76	18·9
26	—	18·0	0·5	0·52	17·5	0·34	56	16·0
27	—	1·9	—	—	1·9	0·34	6	1·7

Present Value Beginning Year 21: $82 million

Table CS6.4
Increment 6 No Stockpile (Mine Limiting)

Year	Cut-off Grade (%)	Tonnage Mined (M)	Tonnage Milled (M)	Average Grade (%)	Copper (000 tonnes)	Cash Flow ($ million)
21	0·27*	18·3	10·9*	0·58*	88	31·9
	0·23	11·7	7·0	0·49		
22	0·23	30·0	17·82	0·49	79	18·0
23	0·23	30·0	17·82	0·49	79	18·0
24	0·23	28·3	16·79	0·49	74	16·6

Present Value Beginning Year 21: $63 million

*End of Increment 5

As all the capital estimates are in the region of $500 million to $700 million, the prospect does not look encouraging. Increases in scale might improve it but the management does not relish the idea of any further financial exposure. Sensitivity studies show that only a substantial strengthening of the price will make the project economic so the decision is taken to continue prospecting but only at a minimum level until such time as the outlook changes.

Stockpiling
It is of interest to examine the stockpiling policy in more detail. For this purpose, the figures for each of the final years beyond year 20 are given in table CS6.3 and table CS6.4. Table CS6.3 includes the recovery of the stockpile as in the Base Case. Table CS6.4 shows the results as they would be without a stockpile.

The existence of the stockpile extends the life by 2½ years and adds $19 million to the present value at the beginning of year 21. However, when discounted back to the beginning of the operation — the start of year 1 — this figure is reduced to $1·2 million. From this perspective, stockpiling is a very doubtful policy. Special facilities have to be prepared and the stockpile, some 50 million tonnes, has to be accumulated during the early years and then kept separate until year 20. The present value cost of this, since much of the expense is incurred at the start, almost certainly exceeds the $1·2 million. In addition, the recovery has been assumed to be the same as that for virgin ore, 90%, even after 20 years. This is a most unlikely eventuality. Nevertheless, considerations other than economics may well dictate the policy.

A comparison of tables CS6.3 and CS6.4 reveals that, without the stockpile, the throughput is constrained by the mining capacity during increment 6. The effect of the stockpile material is to utilise all the mill capacity and even to replace some of the run of mine ore, thus extending the life of the pit. The increase in the annual cash flow is small but the additional years are responsible for most of the benefit. For the final year, only stockpile material is available.

Open Pit — Uranium/Copper

This is a large open pit which has been in operation for a number of years. The mineralisation is complex and the topography is irregular. For these reasons, long-range planning is a very important function and forward pit plans extend to a horizon some 25 years into the future.

Quite detailed plans have been generated in nine increments of between 40 and 50 million tonnes each which together represent approximately the next ten years of production. Beyond this, further plans are in increments of approximately 200 million tonnes to the limits of the ultimate pit which contains, on present estimates, approximately 1,000 million tonnes of material.

It is the practice to review strategic plans every year and for this purpose a rolling ten-year time horizon is adopted. For economic evaluations, detailed annual performances and profits are forecast for each of the ten years, but the value of the remaining life of the operation is then represented by a single residual figure which is effectively a valuation of the remaining reserves ($425 million).

The idea of the strategic review is to confirm the pit development programme, establish a current cut-off grade policy, fix a budget for the coming year and evaluate future improvement and expansion schemes.

The uranium is sold under contracts which impose a maximum delivery of 3,400 tonnes per year. The limit might be lifted to 4,000 tonnes per year in about five years' time, but this is uncertain. One of the capital projects under consideration is a 25% expansion of the mill.

Data

Capacities

Mining	40 million tonnes/year	(M)
Treating	20 million tonnes/year	(H)
Marketing (uranium)	3,400 tonnes/year	(K_1)

Variable unit costs

Mining	$1·20/tonne	(m)
Treating	$3·45/tonne	(h)
Marketing (copper)	$46/tonne	(k_2)

Fixed costs	$20 million	(f)

Prices

Uranium (net)	$50·6/kg	(p_1-k_1)
Copper	$1,760/tonne	(p_2)

Recovery

Uranium	85%	(y_1)
Copper	87%	(y_2)

Cost of capital	10%	(δ)

Residual present value	$425 million

The ore reserve data consists of nine increments, each of which is a table containing the tonnage and average grades of uranium and copper in categories defined by uranium and copper grade intervals. Typical entries are:

U_3O_8 grade interval   0·100-0·125 kg/tonne

Copper Grade Intervals (kg/tonne)	*Tonnes (000)*	*Average U_3O_8 (kg/tonne)*	*Average Cu (kg/tonne)*
0 -0·99	583	0·113	0·62
1·00-1·99	161	0·109	1·56
2·00-2·99	162	0·108	2·68
3·00-3·99	95	0·117	3·80
4·00-4·99	104	0·114	4·68

The complete tables are not included because the individual figures are not of interest in the present context.

Cut-off Policy

On the basis of the best available forecasts for cost, performance and price data, a complete cut-off policy for the next ten years is calculated by applying the OGRE program. The results are summarised in table CS7.1. The present value is $805 million.

As can be seen, the mill is the limiting component of the system throughout. It is operating at full capacity every year. In the early years the mine also is at capacity, but for the last five years the equipment is under-utilised. Only in two years are the maximum deliveries made. Otherwise there is a small shortfall.

The ratios of the net value of uranium and copper are:

$$50 \cdot 6 : (1 \cdot 76 - 0 \cdot 46) = 39 : 1$$

The optimum cut-off intercepts are near this figure except for the two occasions when the market limit for uranium is reached, then it is much less.

One of the improvement schemes under consideration is a mill expansion from 20 million tonnes per year to 25 million tonnes per year. It is proposed that commissioning would be in four years' time just prior to the availability of spare mining capacity.

TABLE CS7.1. COMPLETE CUT-OFF POLICY AT CURRENT CAPACITIES

Period	Limiting Capacity	Cut-off Intercepts (kg/tonne) U_3O_8	Cu	Ratio	Quantities (M tonnes) Mined	Treated	Production (000 tonnes) U_3O_8	Cu	Cash Flow ($ M)
1	MHK_1	0·19	4·8	26:1	40	20	3·4	46	94
2	MH	0·19	6·7	34:1	40	20	3·1	59	98
3	MH	0·19	7·2	37:1	40	20	3·2	60	103
4	MH	0·17	5·9	34:1	40	20	3·1	58	94
5	MH	0·19	7·1	38:1	40	20	3·2	62	107
6	H	0·18	6·9	38:1	35	20	3·3	60	116
7	H	0·18	6·7	38:1	35	20	3·3	57	112
8	H	0·17	6·5	38:1	37	20	3·3	53	103
9	H	0·17	6·3	38:1	38	20	3·3	54	103
10	HK_1	0·16	4·3	26:1	33	20	3·4	54	114

Present Value $805 million

TABLE CS7.2. COMPLETE CUT-OFF POLICY: EXPANDED MILL

Period	Capacity	Limiting Cut-off Intercepts (kg/tonne)		Ratio	Quantities (M tonnes)		Production (000 tonnes)		Cash Flow ($ M)
		U_3O_8	Cu		Mined	Treated	U_3O_8	Cu	
1	MHK$_1$	0·19	4·8	26:1	40	20	3·4	46	94
2	MH	0·19	6·7	34:1	40	20	3·1	59	98
3	MH	0·19	7·2	37:1	40	20	3·2	60	103
4	MH	0·17	5·9	34:1	40	20	3·1	58	94
5	K$_1$	0·18	3·0	17:1	37	23	3·4	66	111
6	K$_1$	0·17	3·0	17:1	32	24	3·4	66	119
7	K$_1$	0·16	3·0	19:1	30	23	3·4	62	117
8	K$_1$	0·15	3·0	20:1	32	23	3·4	54	106
9	K$_1$	0·15	3·0	21:1	34	23	3·4	54	102
10	K$_1$	0·14	3·0	21:1	33	22	3·4	53	107

Present Value $826 million

TABLE CS7.3. COMPLETE CUT-OFF POLICY: EXPANDED MILL WITH MARKET GROWTH

Period	Capacity	Limiting Cut-off Intercepts (kg/tonne)		Ratio	Quantities (M tonnes)		Production (000 tonnes)		Cash Flow ($ M)
		U_3O_8	Cu		Mined	Treated	U_3O_8	Cu	
1	MHK$_1$	0·19	4·8	26:1	40	20	3·4	46	94
2	MH	0·19	6·7	34:1	40	20	3·1	59	98
3	MH	0·19	7·2	37:1	40	20	3·2	60	103
4	MH	0·17	5·9	34:1	40	20	3·1	58	94
5	MH	0·16	5·0	32:1	40	24	3·6	69	121
6	HK$_1$	0·17	5·7	33:1	38	25	3·9	73	141
7	MHK$_1$	0·16	5·5	34:1	39	25	4·0	66	135
8	MH	0·13	6·8	54:1	40	25	3·9	60	122
9	MH	0·12	6·8	54:1	38	25	3·9	60	124
10 (part)	HK$_1$	0·12	3·6	31:1	32	22	3·5	54	118

Present Value $854 million

The effect on the cut-off policy is shown in table CS7.2. Interestingly, the spare mining capacity is not utilised. On the contrary, because of the market limitation, a better tactic is evidently to lower the cut-off grades. This leaves even more mine capacity spare and does not fill the mill either.

The present value improves by $21 million to $826 million. The implication is that the mill expansion is worth undertaking if it can be accomplished at a cost, in present value terms, of less than $21 million. Preliminary estimates indicate that the cost should be substantially less than this.

Another consideration is the possibility of market growth; an increase to 4,000 tonnes U_3O_8 per year in another four years' time is thought likely. In these circumstances, the projected figures and revised cut-off grades would be as shown in table CS7.3. The mine, the mill and the market are more or less in balance from year 5 onwards and the present value improves to $854 million.

Without the mill expansion, none of the benefit of the market growth could be realised. The present mill limitation allows no increase in output. The case for an expansion is therefore probably overwhelming, but in practice it would, of course, have to be subjected to sensitivity analyses to demonstrate the range of conditions under which the scheme remains economic.

Bibliography

Akin H (1983). Determination of recoverable reserves above the cut off by means of the disjunctive kriging method. *Gluckauf – Forshungsh.* Vol. 44 No 4 August 1983, p180-184.

Backwell M R L (1971). Some aspects of the evaluation and planning of the Bougainville copper project in decision making in the Mineral Industry. *CIM* Special Vol. 12, p261-269.

Barnes M (1980). Computer-assisted mineral appraisal and feasibility. New York, *AIME.*

Carlisle D (1954). Economic aspects of the definition of ore. *Trans Inst Min Metall* Vol 64, p89-99, 1954-1955.

Casido C Q (1985). Optimisation of the Amacan open pit. *Asian Mining 1985,* Manila. February 1985, IMM 1985, p239-249.

Dagbert M. Cut-off grades: statistical estimation and reality *CIM Bulletin,* February 1987 Vol 80 No 898, p73-76.

Dowd P (1976). Application of dynamic and stochastic programming to optimise cut off grades and production rates. *Trans Inst Min Metall.* Section A, January 1976 Vol 85, pA22-31.

Elbrond J and Dowd P (1975). The sequence of decisions on cut-off grades and rate of production. 13th *APCOM Symposium,* pS11-13.

Elbrond J *et al* (1977). Rate of production and cut-off grade. A program system for teaching experimentation. 15th *APCOM Symposium,* p13-19.

Habelling H (1931). The economics of exhaustible reserves. *Journal of Political Economy* 39(2), p137-175.

Halls J L, Bellum D P and Lewis C K (1969). Determination of optimum ore reserves and plant size by incremental financial analysis. *Trans Inst Min Metall* Section A 1969 Vol 78, pA20-A30.

Henning ULF (1963). Calculation of cut-off grade. *Can Min Journal* Vol 84(3), p54-57.

Holt W (1961). Some aspects of open pit mining. *Mine and Quarry Engineering* 27 September, 1961, p392-399.

John H T (1984). Cut-off grade calculation for an open-pit mine. *CIMM* Annual General Meeting, Ottawa, April 16-18 1984.

Lane K F *et al* (1984). Cut-off grade for two minerals. 18th *APCOM Symposium,* p485-492.

Lane K F (1979). Commercial aspects of choosing cut-off grades. 16th *APCOM Symposium*, p280-285.

Lane K F (1964). Choosing the optimum cut-off grade. *Colorado School of Mines Quarterly* Vol 59 No 4, p811-829.

Mathieson, G A. Open pit sequencing and scheduling. Presented at *SME-AIME* full meeting Honolulu, Hawaii, September 4-9 1982.

Napier J A L (1983). The effect of cost and price fluctuations on the optimum choice of mine cut-off grades. *Jnl of S Africa IMM.* June 1983, p117-125.

Nils Erin Noren (1971). Mine development – some decision problems and optimization models. *CIM* Special Vol 12, p240-245.

Nilsson D (1982). Optimum cut-off grades in underground mining. *Can Min Journal* Vol 103, p65-70.

Nilsson D and Bengtaaro (1985). Cut-off grade optimisation — a question of bottlenecks and ore reserves. *Inter Min,* July 85, p28-33.

Omer Mol (1984). Cut-off grade determination for mines producing direct shipping ore. *Proc Aust Inst Min Metall* No 289, November-December, p283-287.

Parker H (1979). The volume – variance relationship: a useful tool for mine planning. *EMJ* Vol 180 No 10 October 1979, p106-123.

Pasieka A R and Sotirow G V (1985). Planning and operational cut-off grades based on computerised net present value and net cash flow. *CIM Bull* Vol 78 No 878 June 1985, p47-54.

Plewman R P (1970). The basic economics of open pit mining. *Planning Open Pit Mines.* Johannesburg 1970. Pre-prints 1-8.

Ramos, H C (1977). Impact of grade management on project economics. Symposium Factors affecting mine feasibility studies. School of Mining Engineering, University of New South Wales.

Rudenno V. Determination of optimum cut-off grades. Proceedings of 16th Apcom. *Am Inst of Min Engs,* p261-268.

Schaap W (1981). Effects of mineral grain size and ore hardness on mill-dump cut off grades. *Trans Inst Min Metall.* Section A Vol 90, pA27-33.

Schaap W (1981). A theory of compound decisions on mill-dump cut-off grades. *Geol Mijnbouw,* June 1981, Vol 60 No 2, p237-245.

Schaap W (1983). Cut-off grade theory as a tool for open pit planning. *Erzmetall.* May 1983, Vol 36 No 5, p233-244.

Schaap W (1984). Objective function and methodology in cut-off grade theory. 18th *APCOM, Symposium,* p493-502.

Soderberg A (1959). Elements of long range open pit planning. Min Congr J, April 1959, Vol 45, p54-57 and 62. (*Canada Min Man* 1959, 33, 35, 37, 39, 41).

Taylor H K (1972). General background theory of cut-off grade. *Trans Inst Min Metall,* Section A, July 1972, Vol 81, p160-179.

Taylor H K (1985). Cut-off grades – some further reflections. *Trans Inst Min Metall.* Section A Vol 96, October, pA204-A216.

Thomas E G (1976). Justification of the concept of high–grading metalliferous ore bodies. *Min Mag,* May 1976, Vol 134 No 5, p393-397.

Thomas E G (1977). Justification of high-grading at the feasibility study stage. Symposium Factors affecting mine feasibility studies. School of Mining Engineering. University of New South Wales.

Vickers E L (1961). Marginal analysis – its application in determining cut-off grade. *Mining Eng* 13(6), p578-582.

Watson W B (1962). Flexibility in mine production. *Min and Chem Enging Rev* May 1962, Vol 54, p53-55.

Wells H M (1978). Optimisation of mining engineering design in mineral valuation. *Mining Engineering* December 1978, Vol 30 No 12, p1676-1684.